For Claudia

CONTENTS

INTRODUCTION

*'Though no one can go back and make a brand new start,
anyone can start from now and make a brand new ending.'*
Carl Bard

Having spent over ten years training and working as a psychologist and psychoanalytic psychotherapist, I am naturally fascinated by the mind. While everyone is unique, there is a thread of likeness between each person I have the privilege of working with. In fact, it is part of the human condition. *Our actions and behaviours constantly contradict what we say we want.* This, to my understanding, is evidence of our divided nature. It is never more clearly articulated than in our relationship to our bodies. We say we want to lose weight and get healthy, yet so many people struggle to take action and achieve their goal. What's even more curious about this contradiction is the fact that the people who struggle are adamant that they want to achieve their desired weight. In fact, they spend a lot of time, money and mental energy trying to

do something about it. I know this because I hear it all the time. If you're reading this, it probably sounds very familiar to you too. There is amazing information available now: television shows, blogs, books, scientifically backed diets, supplements, weight-loss clubs, fitness regimes. The list is endless, yet we are on average actually getting bigger. We are constantly told how to lose weight: eat less, eat healthily and move more. Then why isn't that working? Despite the abundance of wonderful healthy-eating advocates, obesity is on the rise.

I think it's time to acknowledge that 'the diet' is dead. Research from UCLA examined a wealth of studies on dieting and found that up to two-thirds of diets fail, with several studies indicating that *dieting is actually a consistent predictor of future weight gain.*[1] One study found that people who participated in formal weight-loss programmes gained significantly more weight over a two-year period than those who had not. So the most likely outcome from going on a diet is ultimately putting on more weight than when you started! This leaves a very small proportion of dieters achieving lasting weight loss. If people actually acknowledged this fact, then I am absolutely sure they would never diet again.

Lasting weight loss is not about what you eat. It's about why and how you eat. As a psychologist and psychotherapist I have come across so many people who are disillusioned and frustrated, feeling guilty about their body and their relationship with food. As a result, people have become obsessed with healthy eating. There are amazing cookbooks and blogs out there communicating the benefits of healthy eating, and while this is a very welcome and positive change, these nutritionists, bloggers and cooks are missing the most vital ingredient in the weight-loss battle: the mind.

By focusing solely on the symptom, the excess weight, we have lost sight of the cause. Take a moment to think about your own relationship with food and your body. When you look in the mirror, what do you see? Do you like the reflection staring back at you? If not, is there any of it that you like? Can you say 'I like my legs, my smile, my hair'? Or are you consumed with negative thoughts about your body? Are the words that come to mind unkind? Do you respect your body? Do you ever take the time to acknowledge how great it is that you can walk, talk, think, dance, work and share your life with friends and family? Or are you too busy thinking about the weight you want to lose, or all the clothes you can't wear because of your size, or all the things you just don't feel comfortable doing until you lose the weight?

I want to introduce you to a client who gave me permission to share her weight struggle. Liz's story really highlights how our issues with weight go way beyond the simple 'calories in, calories out' approach. Liz had tried all kinds of diets, supplements and programmes. A pharmacist in her late twenties, she was well informed about health, how the body works and what she 'should' be doing. Liz came to see me at a point when she realised that, after spending years losing and gaining weight, her life was being controlled by food. She oscillated between being 'good' and only eating diet ready-made meals, and being 'bad' and not sticking religiously to this very strict calorie-controlled regime. Being 'bad' resulted in bingeing, and the inevitable guilt that followed left her feeling low for days, until she returned to the controlled approach. Liz had completely lost touch with her body. This had a very damaging effect on her relationships, as she didn't want anyone to truly know the extent of her struggle. On the surface she came across to friends as being carefree and confident, and kept her unhappiness and food issues completely hidden. Prior to engaging in the Artful Eating philosophy, she described herself as anxious, stressed, down and very self-conscious. She told me that she had withdrawn from social situations, refusing to eat out because she couldn't stick to her diet. Liz was not enjoying food, her body or her life.

Initially I focused on showing Liz how to accept her body. Her preoccupation with the negative aspects of how she looked really affected her relationship with food. It was only by questioning her position and recognising this that she came to understand she needed to reshape her own personal story. Liz was then able to identify unhelpful eating patterns, like controlling what she ate, eating too fast, eating because she felt stressed and not engaging with what she was actually eating. She learned that her relationship with food was not just about the food, but about other issues as well: her self-esteem, her lack of confidence and her inability to be kind to herself. I provided Liz with the skills and tools to help reshape her story, her relationship with food and, most importantly, her relationship with herself. Artful Eating helped Liz escape from masking her issues and identify the underlying cause of her struggle. It allowed her to finally feel a freedom around food and how she felt about herself. She no longer feels anxious around food and she has learned that it's important to declutter and do things that make her feel good now rather than wait to feel good when she reaches her ideal weight. Instead, she learned to be happy and more at ease in herself, both mentally and physically.

Summarising Liz's journey here, it sounds like this was a seamless transition, but she committed to doing the work, she was open to thinking differently and she was ready to approach weight loss in a different way. Sure, she was very nervous when I told her to ditch the diet food and forbade her to calorie count. She was alarmed when I encouraged her to order dessert when she was out with her friends. She was especially worried when I told her to give up the meal plan that she had been clinging to religiously for years, and begin to enjoy food. By taking off the straitjacket, she immediately felt less anxious around food. She completely slowed down and enjoyed food and flavours. As Liz herself wonderfully explains:

> After identifying my habits around food, I now feel more freedom and less anxiety. I do not eat as fast as I did in the past, so I'm enjoying food more. Before eating something, I ask myself if I'm hungry or if there is an emotional trigger to my hunger. I feel more positive and energised, and overall more joyous, as I'm now addressing what my issues are and I am enjoying food rather than having a negative association with it when I'm feeling down. Artful Eating has had a positive impact on my life. I now feel happier, more positive and I'm enjoying my life more without being controlled by food. I am practising my new tools on a daily basis, which have allowed me to engage more freely with people and situations around

me. I have learned to become happy with myself in the present moment, which has allowed me to respect my body for the first time in years. Ultimately I am happier, and less stressed around my body and around food.

This liberation and new-found appreciation for food and your body is exactly what you can expect from reading the chapters to follow. It's time for you to try something different: it's time to love your body and indulge in a little self-love! An alarming number of people disapprove of their body. Depending on which study you refer to, up to 80 per cent of people are on a diet or think they should be. This represents chronic dissatisfaction.[2] How we view ourselves informs everything we do. It's time to learn how to love and respect your body and unblock the psychological barriers to lasting weight loss. If you can't feel good in yourself, then losing the weight isn't drastically going to change that. Studies show that people who win the lottery or become paraplegic revert back to their old thoughts and beliefs after a short period of time. If they were happy and confident before the life-changing experience, they will settle back into that position, and if they were unhappy and unsatisfied with their lot, a lucky windfall or tragic accident won't affect their thinking in the long run.[3]

Being unhappy with how you look and being overweight is a symptom of something *deeper*. Your habits, behaviours, beliefs and the story you tell yourself all contribute to the size you are. Rather than reducing the problem to calories in and calories out, you need to address the issue in a holistic way. I want to show you how to respect your body. Once you do this, the confidence will follow. I personally know that to lose confidence in one's body is to lose confidence in oneself. I have experienced this first-hand and I am so frustrated by the lovely people I meet who are unhappy with their body and unable to enjoy their lives to the full. We only have one life and it seems a terrible waste not to enjoy it.

Let me be very clear here: feeling good in your skin should not be determined by a clothing label, or a number on a set of scales. What's important is that you are happy with the size you are. We all know people who look incredible and stylish and whom we gravitate towards regardless of their size. This is because they are happy and confident and carry themselves that way. This is my desire for you, and weight loss will be a joyous consequence!

There is so much misinformation out there about weight loss. 'Eat this, don't eat that, take this, exercise that way.' But the biggest misconception people have is that if you eat less and move more you will lose weight. The problem is so much deeper and this myth demoralises people, as they feel stupid or lazy because they can't lose weight. In this book you are going to learn how to enjoy food, eat what you want and lose weight, for life. Artful Eating will change the way you think and feel about food and your body. My mission is for everyone to know the truth and to live the truth. Food is an amazing, pleasurable resource that we can and must enjoy. It's time to relearn the joy of eating for pleasure. This is the Artful Eating way of achieving lasting body change and the key to unlocking all your weight issues. Food is not the enemy!

Why is this approach different to all of the fad diets, healthy-eating plans, exercise crazes and diet pills you've tried before? Because I will give you the skills to achieve your weight-loss goal and enjoy a healthy life full of energy and confidence *without dieting*. Successful weight loss is not about what you eat; it's about why and how you eat. It is our mind that fuels every single decision we make about what we eat and how we eat. By changing how we think and feel about our body and the food we eat, we can learn to enjoy food in a whole new way. Only then will you lose weight effortlessly and easily, and keep it off for life. I've taken everything I've learned from ten years of formal studies within the fields of psychology, psychotherapy, psychoanalysis and addiction and my experience as a weight-loss specialist working with amazing people who love this enjoyable way of achieving their dream body and developed a completely different approach to lasting body change. It's a liberation from all the old unhelpful and frankly damaging approaches that simply don't work. I'll provide the knowledge, skills and tools you need, and you will be amazed at how easy it is to achieve the body you desire and truly deserve.

The methods I share in this book are based on the most up-to-date scientific and psychological research and they truly work! I am passionate about what I do. I love empowering my clients and supporting them through their weight-loss journey, and I want that for you too. The Artful Eating philosophy will help you reprogramme your mind to achieve the body you truly desire. I will help you make the right changes, not to what you eat specifically, but to how you think and feel. There is no strenuous exercise regime, no food elimination, no strict meal plan, just powerful psychological tools and strategies that will help you create lasting change.

This book is a guide to the Artful Eating philosophy. It will help you move beyond dieting and restrictive, unhelpful weight-loss fads. Throughout, I will examine the psychological barriers to weight loss and provide practical and actionable steps on how to achieve your ideal size. I have spent over two years developing my online programme and this book is a distillation of that research. This is a how-to guide packed with information backed by research, case studies, stories and recipes: think of it as a lifestyle guide rooted in psychology.

HOW TO USE THIS BOOK

The book is broken down into twelve chapters, with resources spread throughout, followed by a sample week of recipes. Think about each of the chapters as being a spoke on a wheel: all of the elements combine to create the full circle.

This is not an à la carte approach! Everything I ask you to do is absolutely necessary and part of the bigger picture. The whole process will only become clear and make sense once you have completed the book. There are a lot of strategies and actions within these pages and I strongly encourage you to do *every single one*. Some you will be able to do immediately and some you will need to schedule time to do. Once you come across an action that needs time and planning, immediately go to your calendar and carve out that time. If you can't do an action immediately or if it takes a bit of time to complete, please feel free to read on. I have provided timings for each of the actions, but everyone is different and will approach things in their own unique way, so consider the timings as a guide.

I have specifically chosen to share very simple yet delicious recipes with ingredients that are easy to access. I have purposely tried to keep ingredients lists short. The food within these pages is designed to help you learn how to get creative and confident cooking from scratch. Ingredients are easily substitutable so you can adapt recipes to work with whatever you happen to have in your fridge. This will hopefully inspire you to experiment and grow your culinary repertoire.

You must prioritise *yourself* during the Artful Eating journey. While this may seem selfish, the process will make you happier and healthier. Most importantly, the knowledge and skills you are about to learn will be passed on to your family and friends through your actions, behaviours and attitude. You will feel more in control and more at ease in your body, and this healthier way of being will permeate throughout your home! I encourage you to read and reread this book a couple of times and revisit it after a period of weeks, months and years to refresh and replenish your commitment and enthusiasm. We can all get complacent at times, so re-engaging with the information is extremely helpful.

I begin by sharing my own weight challenge in my early twenties, which affected my confidence greatly. It was really this experience that taught me how truly problematic traditional weight-loss approaches are. By sharing my experiences, both personal and professional, throughout this book, I hope to guide you towards finding your own 'artful' way of living, enjoying and being. In psychoanalysis there is a firm understanding that we are singular beings and pushing towards a 'one-size-fits-all' approach is a misconception that ultimately leads to disappointment. I am completely averse to homogenisation, so read the book and take the actions, but make sure that you find a way of applying them that works for you, fits in with your life and feels right. The advice I offer should be adapted to wherever you are in your life. This should be easy to do: just be open-minded, flexible and kind to yourself! Tailor my strategies according to your preferences, environment, schedule and, most importantly, to what your body is telling you!

This approach can be loosely divided into three courses.

STARTER

Become informed and lay a solid foundation for success. As living testimony to the overused adage 'knowledge is power', I will paint the physiological, biological and psychological picture. It's finally time to get informed and honest about your behaviour, habits and unconscious motivations. Prepare your home for a new beginning by conditioning your environment for success. Set your goal and finally let go of the unhelpful and entrenched beliefs about weight loss that have been inhibiting you.

MAIN COURSE

The period of realignment when you will be introduced to the practicalities of how to lose weight while experiencing freedom with food and flavours. Think of this as an education in pleasure as you shift from being controlled and guilty around food to feeling freedom and adventure. The key is to embrace moderation and privilege quality over quantity. During this period, you will begin to lose weight by applying specific strategies, which will quickly become part of the fabric of your life. I'll help you prepare your home for a new beginning, one where you treat your space, body and mind with respect. We will uncover what to eat and precisely *how* to eat it. These are specific techniques, which, once applied, will see you shed the unwanted weight while still having the freedom to enjoy the foods you love. It's important to embrace this period of realignment, because it's not about the destination, it's about the journey. You will also

discover why it is so important to feel good now and to move away from a position of constantly *trying* to lose weight. I will encourage you to embark on an easy lifestyle overhaul that will set you up for success, every day, for life. We will explore exercise, sleep, attitude, lifestyle choices, emotional eating and, most importantly, *food*.

DESSERT

Will introduce you to balance and personal well-being. I'll show you how to become confident and creative in the kitchen. Entertaining will no longer be feared as you learn to love sharing a home-cooked meal accompanied by a delicious glass of wine with good friends. Falling in love with food and flavours will enable you to enjoy indulgences without the guilt or the weight gain.

To help you on your weight-loss journey, I have created a cognitive hypnosis audio bundle, which you can download for free from www.artful-eating.com. The psychological underpinning for the accompanying audios comes from cognitive behavioural therapy (CBT), one of the most validated and researched forms of psychotherapy today. It is extremely effective and is backed up by empirical data and research. It is coupled with a very modern form of hypnotherapy on the audio. This form of hypnosis doesn't rely on relaxation but aims to keep you involved in the process as you accept new suggestions and form new templates for success deep inside your mind. Traditional hypnotherapists rely on suggestion and hypnotisability to create changes in eating,

but with this form of cognitive behavioural hypnosis my focus is to empower and motivate. This book is a guide to the Artful Eating philosophy. It will help you move beyond dieting and restrictive, unhelpful weight-loss fads. I examine the psychological barriers to weight loss and provide practical and actionable steps on how to achieve your ideal size. With this in mind, I encourage you to keep an Artful Eating journal specifically for your responses to the various questions and tasks you will encounter throughout the book. Keeping a journal like this is invaluable and, in the future, it will be wonderful to be able to look back on where you were in your life at the time you wrote it and recognise all the changes you have made since then. Throughout your weight-loss journey I would rather that you are the tortoise, not the hare. Take things slowly, listen to your body and gently make the transition from struggling to thriving.

ARTFUL EATING

STARTER

KNOWLEDGE IS POWER

'The truth will set you free. But first, it will piss you off.' Gloria Steinem

In this chapter you will:
assess the time and money you have spent on weight loss
discover the physiological and biological aspects of weight gain and loss.

When I was twenty-one I moved to London to do a master's degree. It was the first time I properly moved away from home for an extended period. I did move out while doing my undergrad but went home all the time. My mother would bring me food and was still doing my washing, I'm ashamed to admit, so I hadn't fully flown the coop. When I moved to London in 2003, I was excited. My apartment was gorgeous. It was spread out over two storeys at the top of a Georgian house and it had two decent-sized sunny bedrooms with sash windows, and a massive bathroom. Up a little rickety wooden stair into the eves of the house, there was a lovely, bright living room, kitchenette and balcony with a great view of London. It always reminded me of Monica's apartment in *Friends*. I couldn't wait to 'play house'.

Elena, my flatmate, was an Italian American fresh from NYU. She was older and wise to the ways of the world. I enjoyed our year together immensely. We were pretty much inseparable as the two foreigners on the course, and we had a blast. Living together, I took my cues from her in so many ways. She was always there to help and guide me. She taught me how to do the washing and cleaning, essentially becoming my surrogate 'Irish mammy', and taking over the cooking and shopping because I just didn't know how. On the surface she was competent, confident and in control, but deep down she wasn't happy.

Elena had scoliosis and had struggled with her weight for as long as she could remember. Because of the scoliosis she couldn't exercise easily and was often in a lot of pain. From

a young age she was sent to fat camp, a very American solution, which I just could not get my head around. She eventually graduated to 'fat-camp counsellor' and yet she hadn't managed to overcome her own weight issues. So she grew up constantly watching her food. She was permanently on a diet, and as she did all the shopping and cooking, I just fell in with a very different way of eating to anything I had experienced in the past. Fresh from a summer backpacking around Cuba, where I lived on a diet consisting of mainly fresh fish, avocados, mini mangos and bread (while alternating between Cuba libres and mojitos, of course), this new 'healthy weight-loss diet' Elena introduced me to was a real shock to my system.

Breakfast usually consisted of something bland and unimaginative, like bran flakes with skimmed milk, then, for lunch, stir-fried cabbage with balsamic vinegar. I can still taste it now: it was unpalatable! Elena would stir-fry because that was 'healthier' and use balsamic vinegar because you couldn't use oil (oil was fat, and fats were bad, of course). By the end of the day we would be starving and end up eating a whole bunch of rubbish, or order a takeaway from across the road. So began the typical cycle of starting off 'good' and ending up 'bad'. This purge/binge cycle damaged my relationship with food. If it didn't have a diet label we didn't buy it, because it was bad for us. We were eating things like crab sticks (I still don't know what they're made from, but they are not made from crab!), and low-fat bread, milk, cheese and sauces packed our fridge. The food was low on flavour and satisfaction. I stopped eating when I was hungry and became obsessed with the scales.

Instead of losing weight, however, the opposite happened. I became bigger and bigger, and eventually, to my shame, I had to buy new clothes because nothing would fit me. I just couldn't understand what was happening. To top it all off, I was also taking an array of supplements Elena recommended that she'd brought over from the US to help me lose weight. But actually I was piling it on. I was constantly thinking about food. Worrying, scratching my head and wondering why I was putting on all this weight instead of losing it. I was miserable. I loved living with Elena, I loved being in London, but I did not feel good in my skin and I was no longer my carefree, confident self. I felt uncomfortable in social situations, especially with people I didn't know. If you had asked me though, I would have said I was trying really hard to lose weight and I just didn't know what was going wrong. But the truth is I was doing everything wrong. *The number-one thing was dieting.*

After finishing up my master's degree, I immediately moved home, much to the shock of my friends, who hadn't seen me for a year (I had stayed in most of the Christmas break, embarrassed about my sudden weight gain). They were really surprised at my size and I remember telling myself: 'I'm home and I'm putting it all behind me.' I didn't rush to go on some sort of diet; I just started to breathe. I returned to enjoying my mother's home cooking and her wonderful vegetable soup (you'll find the recipe in Chapter 12), which she encouraged me to eat for lunch every day. I began to focus on other things: I got a job, met a guy, found a place to live. As soon as I stopped dieting, as soon as I stopped worrying about what I was putting into my mouth, and as soon as I started eating food I actually liked and enjoyed, the weight literally fell off. And it fell off quite quickly: within eight to ten months, I was back to my normal size.

Diets don't work. In fact, the most likely outcome from being on a diet is putting on weight. This is exactly what I and so many other people can attest to. You probably can too! This book seeks to understand why diets don't work and to provide you with a sustainable way to lose weight and maintain that weight loss *without dieting*. But let's see if you find this statement to be true on a personal level, before we get into the hard facts.

ACTION #1: ASSESSMENT (10 MINUTES)

In a survey of 3,000 British women it was found that they on average will spend £25,000 (€28,500) on weight loss over their lifetime.[1] That's a lot of money! It is hard to quantify the amount of money, mental energy and emotional suffering a person goes through struggling with their size, but if you can, try to. Get a pen and paper, and take a few minutes to add up how much time, money and energy you have spent to date on trying to lose weight.

HOW MUCH MONEY HAVE YOU SPENT ON:

- *fad diets*
- *special ingredients or supplements*
- *food elimination programmes, weight-loss pills*
- *exercise machines and accessories*
- *exercise or weight-loss classes*
- *gym memberships*
- *diet clubs*

HOW MUCH TIME THROUGHOUT A DAY DO YOU SPEND:

- *not feeling happy with how you look*
- *not feeling confident in your clothes*
- *thinking about food*
- *vowing to lose weight*
- *feeling guilty about what you have eaten*
- *battling with yourself not to eat something or to give in and eat something*
- *feeling physically uncomfortable in your body*

Try roughly adding up the minutes. If you find it difficult to quantify, a rough 'guesstimate' will do. The point is that by asking and taking the time to attempt to answer these questions, you can begin recognise that there is most likely a persistent stream of negative thoughts and behaviours around food and your body. Surprising, isn't it? We spend so much time feeling guilty and unhappy with our weight and our relationship with food. But this position is simply compounding the problem.

The English philosopher Francis Bacon is believed to have said: 'Knowledge is power', and as someone who has two degrees, a higher diploma, three master's and is currently engaged in a PhD, I am a firm believer in this! I want to empower you with helpful information so that you can come to understand your body in a new and exciting way. We are more inclined to do something if we understand why we are doing it, so I'm going to talk about the physiology and psychology of weight loss.

We like to expect that if we put in the effort to lose weight, our bodies will respond in kind. Unfortunately, it just doesn't work that way, as you can see from the previous exercise. Diets only work so long as we absolutely stick to them: as soon as we stop, we pile back on all the weight. So it's really important for you to recognise that Artful Eating must be a lifelong lifestyle shift, not a short-term tool for weight loss.

WHERE DOES THE WEIGHT YOU LOSE GO?

Where does the weight you lose go? Do you excrete it? Do you burn it up as energy? I bet most of you have never even thought about this question, but it's a really important one when you are in the process of losing weight. In answering it, I look to physicist Dr Ruben Meerman.[2] He explains that 'C55 H104 O6' is the composition of an average fat molecule. This is a combination of carbon, hydrogen and oxygen. Our body absorbs the nutrients from the food we eat, and what we excrete is the remainder, the matter that we haven't absorbed. What we excrete has nothing to do with weight loss, because it was only ever passing through. The stuff we extract from the food we eat is what's turned into fat molecules. So how does this stuff get out of our body?

$$FAT + OXYGEN = CARBON$$
$$DIOXIDE + WATER$$

Just think about this: weight loss is achieved through breathing out carbon dioxide and water. Carbon dioxide is a gas, so our weight loss is sweated, peed and breathed out of us. Why am I telling you this? I want you to be as educated as possible about your body. I want you to begin to understand and listen to how your body works. We have become so alienated from our bodies that we no longer are in tune with what our body needs and how it process things.

DO YOU KNOW HOW YOUR BODY AND MIND REACT TO WEIGHT LOSS?

Recognising how the brain responds to dieting helps us understand why losing weight can be so challenging. We know that our weight depends on how much we eat and how much energy we burn, but the important thing to realise is that hunger and energy usage are both controlled by the brain. So while you may have committed to losing weight, your brain has other ideas! The neuroscientist Sandra Aamodt first introduced me to the concept that our body acts like a thermostat.[3] The brain naturally establishes a 'set-point': this is the weight range of between 10 and 15 lb that your body is comfortable within. While your lifestyle choices can move your weight up or down, it is actually quite challenging to move outside of your set-point, because the brain fights to stay within this weight range, regardless of how overweight you are.

The hypothalamus, the part of the brain that regulates your body weight, controls more than a dozen chemical signals that tell your body to gain or lose weight. This system responds to the signals and adjusts hunger, metabolism and activity to keep your weight stable as conditions change. This process mirrors a thermostat that keeps the temperature in your house stable as the weather outside changes. When you try to change the temperature in your house by opening a window, the thermostat responds by turning on the furnace to maintain the same level of heat.

Your brain works in exactly the same way. When you begin to limit your food intake, your brain responds by adjusting hunger, metabolism and activity in an effort to maintain your set-point. So when you reduce your calorie intake on a diet, you become hungrier and your muscles burn less energy. This happens regardless of whether you start off fat or thin. Research has found that people who have lost 10 per cent of their body weight burn 250 to 400 fewer calories a day because their metabolism is suppressed.[4] What this means is that to maintain your weight loss when dieting you need to eat that much less consistently, not just while you're on the diet.

Your body's resistance to weight loss makes complete sense from an evolutionary perspective. Over the course of human history, starvation has been a much bigger problem than overeating, and in the past our bodies' resistance to weight loss was an advantage; indeed, it still is in parts of the world where food is scarce. In these circumstances our survival depends on our body conserving energy and an ability to quickly regain weight when food becomes available again. It is this very fact that leads us to something we have probably already experienced after giving up on yet another diet: your set-point can go up, but it is much harder for it to go down, as you are fighting against your innate functionality.

Unfortunately, successful dieting doesn't necessarily lower your set-point. Research shows that even after you have kept the weight off for as long as seven years, your brain pushes to try and gain the weight back. Now, if the weight loss had been due to a famine, this would make sense. When trying to lose weight, we need to take into account this resistance and understand that the most effective solution to obesity is to change both our relationship with what we eat and with our food environment. I am telling you this not to dishearten you, but to empower you! In order to work with your biology, you need to change your eating behaviour, your thoughts and your approach to weight loss.

Psychologists classify eaters into two groups:

- **Intuitive eaters:** people who listen to their body and eat when they are hungry

- **Controlled eaters:** people who try to control their eating through willpower, like most dieters

Intuitive eaters are less likely to be overweight and they spend less time thinking about food because they eat when they are actually hungry, whereas controlled eaters are much more vulnerable to overeating, as they constantly override their bodies' hunger signals in an effort to try to lose weight. When you are in a pattern of controlled eating, a small indulgence, like a piece of cake, is actually more likely to lead to a food binge.

So, how can you shift from being a controlled eater to an intuitive eater? By learning to understand your body's signals so that you eat when you're hungry and stop when you're full, because a lot of weight gain boils down to eating when you're not hungry. I love seeing my clients accomplish this shift. When you train yourself to really listen to your body and eat intuitively you will find that you eat a lot less than you think you need to. Also, once you learn to listen to your body and understand that you really can eat what you want, you will become so much more relaxed around food.

THE TRUTH ABOUT OUR GENETICS

In the UK, 62 per cent of adults are currently either overweight or obese, and in the USA this figure increases to 66 per cent, which is really quite shocking.[5] Yet despite millions of pounds being invested in spreading the message 'eat less and move more' throughout the UK and USA, we are getting fatter year on year. This is because the reasons people eat more are very complex. Cambridge geneticist Dr Giles Yeo has found that for some people eating less is more challenging than for others.[6] We know that there are over 100 genes linked to obesity. Of these, the one with the largest effect is a gene called the 'fat mass and obesity-related transcript', or FTO. While all of us have FTO, some of us have inherited a slightly different version of the gene, which increases our risk of becoming obese. Half of the population have a version of FTO that contains one small change. What this means is that people who have this one change to their FTO gene are on average 3.3 lb heavier and 25 per cent more likely to become obese. But roughly one in six of us are unlucky enough to have two small changes, or a

double-risk variant of FTO, and they are more likely to want to eat even more. People with the double-risk variant of FTO are on average 6.6 lb heavier and they are typically 50 per cent more likely to become obese.

These genetic variations have been linked to changes in the brain that make it less sensitive to appetite hormones released from the gut and fat cells. People with the FTO risk variants are biologically programmed to not feel full as quickly as those without it. While this was a huge survival advantage in the past, when food was scarce, it is a disadvantage now that many of us live in a place of food abundance. Eating behaviours associated with this FTO variant include eating larger portions and favouring calorie-dense foods that are high in fat and sugar.

While this may sound disheartening, it is important to understand that you can still win at poker even if you have been dealt a bad hand! I'm sharing this with you so that you are informed. Perhaps you don't recognise when you feel satiated due to your genetics, but this does not mean that you can't change your behaviours, attitudes and relationship to food and your body. Based on the average extra weight of people with the single and double FTO variant, which is either only 3.3 lb, or 6.6 lb, there are many people out there with one of these gene variants that are not overweight at all. Our genes do not determine us.

Interesting scientific solutions are being proposed to address the obesity epidemic.

Researchers from the Alpert Medical School are investigating the effects of transplanting gut bacteria on our weight.[7] This procedure emerged after a slim patient was being treated for a stomach infection by receiving an injection of gut bacteria from her overweight but otherwise healthy daughter. This resulted in the patient, who had always been slim, gaining more than four stone over the space of two years! This indicated that the weight gain could have been due to the foreign bacteria from her daughter.

Although in this case the patient's weight gain was an unfortunate side effect of a procedure intended to rectify her stomach complaint, it has inspired doctors to try the same procedure but in the hope of the opposite result. The proposed transplanting procedure involves the introduction of faecal matter of lean, healthy people, along with its 'good' gut flora, through the rectum and into the large and small intestines of obese patients. The aim is to replace the microbes present in overweight people's colons with 'metabolically healthy' microbes that should make them feel full after a meal. I will address the importance of healthy gut microbes in Chapter 5, but I just want to inform you about what cutting-edge science is championing in an effort to tackle obesity.

Another arguably less-invasive procedure to tackle obesity is now being encouraged instead of a gastric-band procedure. This process involves injecting overweight people with hormones replicating those found in thin people. These hormones send a message to the brain to switch off the supply of food, and they seem to be effective. The injection mimics gastric-bypass surgery by tricking subjects into feeling full, but this method is much more preferable than gastric-band surgery, which is a relatively effective method of weight loss but is expensive and carries a 1 in 200 risk of death. Sir Steve Bloom, Professor of Medicine at Imperial College, London, claims that if we fast forward ten years obesity won't be a problem.[8] He believes that people with weight issues will have these injections that will simply suppress the appetite and result in weight loss. In tests, two obese men injected with these hormones ate around 280 fewer calories at their next meal. Sir Bloom's fellow researcher Patricia Tan found that with the injections of the hormones subjects ate up to 30 per cent less. The process involves three hormones, OXM, PYY and GLP1, being administered with an injection before each meal, but the scientists hope to develop an injection that lasts for a week.

These are some of the very compelling new 'solutions' to the obesity problem, but I am convinced they are missing the mark because they fail to take into account the influence of the mind. Let me distinguish here between the mind and the brain. The mind is not biological; it's psychological. It is that part of us where our thoughts, beliefs and emotions reside. While science does an excellent job focusing on and working with the brain and the biological, in my opinion it fails to privilege the psychological. In order to overcome your genetic or physical disadvantages you need to focus on the psychological tools, thoughts and beliefs that ultimately determine your choices and behaviours.

Think about this: how much is your weight issue due to eating because you feel hungry and how much is due to eating when you are not hungry? These medical procedures address the issue of suppressing our hunger, but that is really only part of the issue. People who struggle with their weight eat when they are sad, tired, bored, lonely, stressed, unhappy, happy, celebrating, emotional, self-sabotaging, bingeing, angry . . . the list goes on! So this is not about reducing the problem to biology; it's about understanding our own relationship with food and our bodies. It's about developing positive healthy habits, making good decisions and fostering a sustainable approach to achieving and maintaining your ideal body.

Throughout the book you will be asked lots of interesting questions about your relationship with food, your thoughts and how you view yourself. Please take the time to answer all of these questions. They really are important because they will help you to uncover the underlying cause of your unhappiness with your body and find the motivation and conviction to create lasting change. This knowledge has empowered you to make the first major shift in your mindset and Artful Eating will help you achieve the change you desire, but only if you commit to doing each of the actions you encounter throughout this book.

2

MIND AND BODY AWARENESS

'It is not the mountain we conquer, but ourselves.' Sir Edmund Hillary

In this chapter you will:
reflect on all the reasons you want to lose weight and enjoy your body
become honest with yourself and assess where you are going wrong with what and how you eat
learn about the psychological and environmental factors which greatly influence the success or failure of any weight-loss approach
discover the key ingredients to successful weight loss from a psychological perspective.

To successfully lose weight and keep it off, it is essential to begin to understand that it is not so much about *what* you eat as it is about *why* you eat. The questions, actions and information in this chapter will help you to get to know the part of you that causes you to overeat, so take your time to reflect and thoughtfully answer the questions provided in as much detail as possible. It is only by understanding why you eat and how you eat that you can begin to change your eating habits and your relationship with food, permanently.

ACTION #1: WHY DO YOU WANT TO LOSE WEIGHT? (10 MINUTES)

Here are some of the common reasons people want to lose weight. Check off each one according to how important it is to you (1: not really that important to 10: very important to me).

- *I will look better.*
- *I will feel healthier.*
- *I will be more attractive to others.*
- *I will be able to wear anything I like.*
- *I will like what I see when I look in the mirror.*
- *I won't feel so self-conscious.*
- *I will be able to exercise without feeling embarrassed or uncomfortable.*
- *I will live longer.*
- *I will have more energy.*
- *I will be more physically fit.*
- *I will enjoy sexual intimacy more.*
- *I will like myself more.*
- *I will feel more in control of my life.*
- *I will have more confidence.*
- *I won't be so hard on myself and so critical of myself.*
- *I will be more outgoing.*
- *I will do more things.*

- *I won't have anyone annoying me about my weight.*
- *I won't have people commenting on what I eat.*
- *I will feel more comfortable eating in front of others.*
- *I won't be thinking about food all the time.*
- *I won't crave 'bad' foods so much.*
- *I won't struggle with what I should eat all the time.*
- *I won't feel guilty if I eat something I shouldn't.*

Any other reasons? Write down every single benefit you can think of, even the smallest and silliest of reasons.

ACTION #2: REFLECTIONS (10 MINUTES)

Take some time to thoughtfully answer the questions below in as much detail as possible. I encourage you to actually write out your answers, as you will be able to return to them at a later point and see how much your mindset has changed. Also, the act of writing will help to untangle your thinking and give you some insight into this issue.

WHAT, IN YOUR OPINION, HAS STOPPED YOU FROM LOSING WEIGHT?

WHEN DO YOU THINK YOU ARE MOST LIKELY TO OVEREAT?

DO YOU EAT FOR ANY OF THE FOLLOWING REASONS?

- *self-reward*
- *stress*
- *anger*
- *boredom*
- *depression*
- *anxiousness*
- *worry*
- *loneliness*
- *comfort*
- *punishment*

DO YOU EAT FOR ANY OTHER EMOTIONAL REASONS?

ACTION #3: DISCOVERY WEEK (1 WEEK, 15 MINUTES A DAY)

Denial is a big issue when it comes to weight, so we really need to take the time to do the work and get honest with ourselves. Please do not skip this step!

For the next week, journal everything you eat and drink, and keep a record of when you eat and how much you spend on food.

The information you compile here will be crucial when we come to realignment, which is the process of achieving your goal weight or size. It is important to get a proper idea of what you're actually ingesting and how much you're spending on food. When the week is up, come right back to this section of the book to analyse your week. You can of course continue reading on, but you have to invest the time and effort in this initial assessment week.

Once you've completed the week, let's get analysing:

1. WHAT ARE YOUR MAJOR FOOD PITFALLS? (HIGHLIGHT YOUR FOOD PITFALLS IN RED.)

- *white bread*
- *chocolate*
- *sweets/sugary snacks*
- *alcohol*
- *crisps*
- *eating out*
- *diet or sugary drinks*

2. WHAT ARE YOUR MAJOR TIME PITFALLS? (HIGHLIGHT YOUR TIME PITFALLS IN RED.)

- *Do you find yourself snacking late at night?*
- *Do you find yourself grazing throughout the day?*

Do you find that you do relatively well during the week but at the weekend you drink too much and overindulge?

3. HOW MUCH DO YOU RELY ON PROCESSED AND PRE-PACKAGED FOODS? (HIGHLIGHT ALL THE PROCESSED FOODS YOU HAVE EATEN IN RED.)

Processed food is any food that is created or assembled by radically non-traditional means, especially using industrial or chemical processes that did not exist when the original recipe was developed and/or bear little resemblance to the methods a home cook or baker might use to create a similar product. How much do you rely on processed and pre-packaged foods?

- *sauces*
- *breads*
- *ready meals*
- *sweet treats*
- *industrially made yogurts*
- *cheeses*
- *meats*

4. HOW MUCH OF YOUR FOOD JOURNAL IS FILLED WITH MINDLESS EATING OR UNNECESSARY FOOD? (HIGHLIGHT THESE IN RED.)

- *eating when you were not hungry*
- *eating something you didn't really want*

- *eating something that you didn't need*
- *eating something that wasn't nourishing*
- *eating something you didn't enjoy*
- *eating something due to boredom*
- *emotional eating*
- *eating because you were offered it*
- *eating because you were treating yourself as opposed to nourishing yourself*

Be as honest as possible, as this is the point of this first exercise!

Next, check your positive food choices.

5. HOW MUCH OF YOUR FOOD JOURNAL IS FILLED WITH WHOLE FOODS? (HIGHLIGHT THE WHOLE FOODS IN GREEN.)

Whole food is the opposite of processed food. It is food that has been processed or refined as little as possible and is free from additives or other artificial substances. We will talk about this in more detail later on, but for now just go with what you would consider to be whole or healthy foods.

6. HOW MUCH IS YOUR FOOD JOURNAL FILLED WITH POSITIVE, NOURISHING FOOD CHOICES? (MARK THESE IN GREEN.)

- *nourishing food that filled you up*

- *satisfying food that you really enjoyed*

- *food you ate when you were actually hungry (this final one may overlap with red-highlighted foods, but I want you to try and make a note, if you can remember, of times you ate when you actually felt hungry)*

7. MONEY

How much did you spend on food? Did you make many impulse purchases, like a latte or cappuccino? A pastry at break time, a chocolate bar or a packet of crisps with your coffee break? How much did you spend on eating out or takeaways? What do you spend most of your food budget on? Alcohol? Eating out? Impulse purchases? Convenience purchases? Add up how much you have spent on impulse and convenience purchases this week.

Eating well does not mean that you have to spend a fortune, but it does mean that you have to consciously choose where to spend your food budget. A takeaway cappuccino from a world-famous coffee chain costs approximately £3.20 (€3.60). This is approximately £16 (€18) a week, the price of a medium vegetable box from my local organic supermarket, which feeds the family for a week. Studies show that the average Briton spends £110.00 on takeaways per month![1] Again, this is money that would do

well to go toward healthier, tastier ingredients and foods. Certainly food for thought.

8. REFLECTIONS

Assess your food journal. What is the ratio of red to green?

If you find that your weekly list is predominantly red, then you can clearly see where things are going wrong.

If your list is mostly green, as in whole healthy foods, then portion size might be an issue for you.

Take some time and write down your reflections on this exercise. Try not to filter your thoughts, just take a few minutes and write whatever comes to your mind.

Once you have analysed your eating habits, it's time to start realigning your mind and body. I am going to teach you the essential healthy habits that will reprogramme your mind's approach to food. This is the really exciting part. The exercises I'm going to ask you to incorporate into your daily routine will be the key to reprogramming your mindset and behaviours. You can probably see from discovery week that your weight issues go way beyond the simple 'calories in, calories out' model. You can see that the type of food you eat, when you eat and why you eat have a huge determination over your weight issues. You need to consider the psychological aspects of weight loss, not just the biological, as psychology has a lot to teach us about why diets fail in the long term.

THE PSYCHOLOGICAL ASPECT OF WEIGHT ISSUES

Today, 44 per cent of the diabetes burden, 23 per cent of the heart disease burden, and up to 41 per cent of cancer burdens are linked to obesity. [2] These are shocking statistics. We know that weight gain has some serious physical health consequences and is a cause of great concern for governments, as the pressure being put on healthcare services is immense. But what about the personal psychological consequences?

My clients regularly tell me that when they don't feel happy with their body they struggle to feel confident. I had a client, Katherine, who was carrying over four stone of extra weight. She had been overweight since her early teens and each year a few more pounds appeared. Katherine had tried every diet going and had finally come to me, hoping for some magical solution. She was in a very bad way emotionally and I could see that she was depressed. Consumed by how much weight she had to lose, she struggled to believe that she could actually achieve her desired size.

There are so many people like Katherine who are severely unhappy with their body, yet they just can't lose the weight. She had tried all sorts of diets and 'lose weight quick' solutions, but she was constantly focusing on calorie counting or appetite suppressants, and failed to think about the psychological aspects of her issue. The diets she tried all had the same focus: food intake and exercise.

A recent survey asked dieters what their weight-loss goal was. The average dieter said that they wanted to lose about 55 lb. After twelve months of eating less, the dieters had lost on average 12 lb: significantly less than their goal. Furthermore, out of everyone that began dieting, only 50 per cent were still making the effort to lose weight after twelve months. This research indicates that our expectations do not align with reality. Our expectations are perpetuated by the media and 'lose weight fast' programmes as we try to lose weight with sheer willpower alone. From a psychological standpoint, we set ourselves up to fail – and I'm going to explain why.

Most dieters, like Katherine, engage in diets that are structured around deprivation, relying on controlled eating. So Katherine regularly found herself saying, 'I'm not going to eat the thing that I love because I am trying to lose weight.' This is a position of self-punishment to which we eventually concede defeat. While some people can maintain this position longer than others, ultimately they fail because they are fighting against their brain's natural disposition to seek out pleasure and avoid pain. Prohibiting the things we love to eat will simply never work. And this is why Katherine failed again and again. In trying to avoid certain foods or sticking to a limiting meal plan, she was relying on self-control.

This approach works from the premise that if we have enough willpower, weight loss will be easy. But what significant psychological research indicates is that we seem to have only a finite amount of self-control.[3] Think of willpower like a muscle: when you use it, you get tired. This is exactly what happens with self-control. When you exert self-control you become fatigued. This is called 'ego depletion'. When we experience ego depletion we are less able to use self-control again. Katherine described to me how this cycle happened to her repeatedly over a fifteen-year period. Every summer she would embark on a slimming-down regime and every autumn she would give in and ultimately give up, fed up of staving off the things she loved.

I explained to Katherine why this kept happening. I explained how dieting, sticking to a strict meal plan that eliminated things she loved, required her to heavily rely on the psychology of thought suppression, or what's known as the 'white-bear effect'. The white-bear effect is a simple premise: when you are told not to think about a white bear, all you end up thinking about is . . . a white bear! So every time Katherine decided to try and slim down for the summer, naturally all she could think about were the foods she wasn't supposed to eat.

This is evident when it comes to cravings. If you tell yourself 'I can't have that takeaway curry because it's not allowed on my diet programme', then all you can think about is the curry. This happens because when we try to suppress a thought, on a preconscious level (that part of the mind that lies just below the level of our immediate conscious awareness) we then must scan for the thought that we are trying to suppress, which means that we have to be aware what the thought actually is. So it keeps popping up in our consciousness and then we have to keep supressing it. This is a very tiring process.

So when you're trying to lose weight and the curry thought keeps popping up, I want you to acknowledge the thought. You must indulge your thoughts and cravings in a positive way. You can have a curry, or whatever the food you crave is. Say to yourself, 'I'm going to make it myself, it will be full of healthy, non-processed, natural, good-quality ingredients and it's going to taste delicious.' This is a much healthier approach, and I will go into more detail about how to do this in Chapter 9 and 10.

Now that we have explored the many reasons why diets fail, let's have a look at what psychological research can teach us about successful dieting. Firstly, and most importantly, people who successfully lose weight and keep it off don't see themselves as being on a diet. They do not undergo deprivation and self-punishment because this is not sustainable in the long term. They do not battle with themselves on a daily basis to avoid foods they love. Instead they see it as a positive lifestyle change. Once Katherine moved away from a weight-loss approach that focused on deprivation and controlled eating, she stepped off the yo-yo diet treadmill and started to steadily lose weight. By shifting from over-intellectualising what she could eat and when, to eating when she was actually hungry and being present, enjoying her food and stopping when she had enough, she started to respect her body and act in line with her goal. It took a bit longer than she would have liked, but the weight came off slowly and steadily. (I always encourage my clients to be the tortoise, not the hare.) As the weight slowly dissolved, Katherine's mindset and lifestyle had time to change too.

So think about making changes in your life, to the way you think and the way you behave. Successful weight loss is about treating your body well, with positivity and kindness. It's about improving your life, not just losing weight. Psychological research has proved that to successfully lose weight and keep it

off, a personalised approach works best. Focus on eating the foods that you like and doing the exercise that you enjoy. Make sure it fits easily into your schedule, commitments and preferences. This is why I don't prescribe any specific food plan. You can eat anything as long as you seek out the best quality you can afford and avoid overly processed foods. Finally, psychological research shows that to achieve successful weight loss and to maintain it you need the right support, the right advice and the right strategies to deal with things that make weight loss difficult. Again, this is something that we will work on throughout the book.

ACTION

'Everything you can imagine is real.'
'Action is the foundational key to all success.' Pablo Picasso

In this chapter you will:
set your goal and believe you can achieve it
learn about conditioning (not body conditioning!)
decide to take action
finally let go of all the old inhibiting beliefs about weight loss.

This chapter is all about getting into the right frame of mind to achieve your ideal size. There is no strict food regime involved in the Artful Eating philosophy; however, moving forward you are going to change your relationship with and your understanding of food, for ever. Before we get started, I have an exercise that will help you to get into the right mindset for change.

ACTION #1: VISUALISATION (5 MINUTES)

First, go to www.artful-eating.com to access your audio recording of this visualisation exercise in the free Artful Eating audio bundle.

Visualisation works. This is something that the sports industry has been taking advantage of for years. First, let me be clear about what visualisation is. Take a minute and think of a lemon. A bright-yellow lemon. I want you now to imagine cutting the lemon in half. Put the lemon to your lips and taste the tartness. Does it taste sour? You've just visualised something!

When we visualise an action and when we actually perform that action, the same regions of the brain are stimulated. So with that example of seeing, cutting and tasting a lemon, the parts of your brain that would be stimulated by going through that process in reality were stimulated even though you were just thinking it. Scientific literature has extensively demonstrated this process of brain activation. Dr Pillay of the NeuroBusiness Group provides a compelling example of stroke victims who have lost the power of their limbs, thus diminishing the limbs' blood supply; however, when these stroke victims simply visualise (or imagine) using the paralysed limbs, they can save the brain tissue that surrounds the damaged tissue where blood flow has been compromised.[1]

This is a very simple yet effective exercise that will take a couple of minutes. Read through the exercise first or download the free audio, and then take the time to do it now. Find a quiet space and take a deep breath in and out. Settle yourself comfortably and take a moment to think about your future.

What will happen if you continue on the same path and don't make the changes you need to attain the body you desire? It is important to really recognise the damage and devastation inaction will bring if you don't change your approach to food and your body now. Take a moment and picture yourself in a year's time continuing on the same path you have been on, not taking action. You are standing in front of a full-length mirror looking at your reflection. What do you look like and what are you wearing? Or are you naked? How do you feel? Have you gotten bigger? How is your health? Are you physically uncomfortable? Do you feel confident and happy? Is this a positive image and are you

satisfied with what you see? Or do you feel frustrated and uncomfortable in your clothes?

Make the image as clear as you can in your mind. See what you can see and feel how it feels. Really take the time to visualise this scene and feel the emotions that come with still being in this position.

Now take a minute and visualise yourself in a year's time, having taken action and achieved your goal. See the amazing benefits that taking action now will bring to you and your family in the near future. Again, you are looking in a full-length mirror. How do you look? What are you wearing? How do you feel? Fit, healthy and confident? Are you smiling? Do you like what you see? Imagine stepping into the image in the mirror and embodying this slim, gorgeous new frame. You feel lighter, more comfortable and at ease in your body. You feel full of energy and confidence.

Really take the time to see and feel the benefits of taking action and making lasting changes.

Right now you can take the action required to create a future where you experience a healthy balanced environment for you and your family. You can make your dream of a happy, healthy, beautiful body, inside and out, a reality. These are not exaggerated claims. They are truly achievable goals. Now it is time to get your mind prepared for a new beginning. In this chapter we will get very clear on what you are committing to. Once you know exactly what you want to achieve it is much easier to start acting in line with that goal.

We can spend a lot of time thinking about doing something. When you did that first exercise in Chapter 1, were you surprised at how much time you spent thinking about losing weight? If only we could manage to put that much time and energy into actually taking action and achieving our goal. When people call me to book an appointment, they are often quite nervous. It can take a long time to pick up the phone and make that call. Months, sometimes even years, will go by before people are ready to take action and start to change, even if that change is what you want and will have a positive impact on your life.

The strange thing is, we are really good at encouraging change in others and we are excellent at doing the difficult things for our partners, children and pets. When we think about making changes and moving towards something for ourselves, it can feel very daunting. But it really doesn't need to be. I remember when my sister Alana, my now husband Liam and I bought our first house. It was our grandfather's home and it hadn't been touched since our grandmother died some thirty years before. It was a beautiful, large, rambling semi-detached house with an incredible long south-facing garden. Overwhelmed and with a very small budget, we started stripping wallpaper and pulling up carpets.

Thinking back on that six-bedroom house now, trying to get it to a point that I was happy with could have been overwhelming, and at times it was. But I did not look at the house as a whole. We started in one room and slowly worked our way through the house, gradually ticking things off the list. Instead of spending time focusing on all the things we had yet to do, I would experience extreme pleasure from looking at what we had achieved. When a wall had been completely stripped of its 1980s floral paper and a fresh coat of bright paint had taken its place, I would feel immense joy and pride. Not once did I look at the project as a whole. I'm sure if I had, I would have given up. Instead I focused on one room at a time. We definitely didn't have enough money at the time to do all the things we wanted to do and do them to a standard that we would have liked. But my attitude then, as it still is now, is that it doesn't have to be perfect, it just has to get done.

I had a vision for what I wanted to achieve and was determined to do so. Not making that house a beautiful home was simply not an option. We came up with all sorts of ingenious ways of getting the project done. We discovered liquidation sales and bought some beautiful antique furniture, which I still cherish today. We roped in help from all sides, and the house slowly revealed its beauty. The most important thing about that process is that I enjoyed it, even though it was challenging, physically arduous and dangerous at times. I have to say we made a few expensive mistakes, but in the end everyone agreed it was a beautiful home. And we loved it, until it was time to sell up and move on to the next challenge!

Change is a wonderful and exciting thing. It doesn't need to be feared. Having the right attitude is essential when it comes to achieving your goal. This process, while challenging at times, must be framed as enjoyable and positive. I always had a clear vision for what that house could look like. While trying to sand the old floorboards, I was thinking of how beautiful they would look when the room was complete. I always focused on the end point and how fantastic it would feel when the whole house was finished. This is a key aspect of achieving your goal.

ACTION #2: SET YOUR GOAL (5 MINUTES)

Decide what your goal is. It's important to be specific, whether it's a weight or size you were in the past when you felt confident and comfortable with your body, or maybe it's a specific outfit you want to fit into. Perhaps it's your idea of the perfect set of measurements. Maybe you can't remember a time when you felt absolutely fabulous in your body: that's okay too. Pick a person who has a body you admire and choose that as your goal. But remember, it must be specific. The most important thing is that this goal feels realistic to you. If you don't truly feel that you can achieve this goal, then it will forever be an impossibility. So you may need to pick an interim goal to start with to help you to acclimatise to the idea of changing your size. Take some time now to assess and decide what your goal is.

Now close your eyes and visualise looking in the mirror, having achieved your goal. How does it feel? Are you smiling? Feeling confident? Are you full of vitality and wearing the clothes you want to wear? Step into that image in your mind so that you are embodying this new you. Feel those good feelings; enjoy feeling lighter, happier and more confident. Use the accompanying free audio at www.artful-eating.com to help you with this visualisation.

Establishing a goal is the first step towards committing to a new way of being and achieving your ideal size.

ACTION #3: CONDITIONING (30 MINUTES)

I'm not talking about body conditioning; I mean conditioning your mind for success! Start to reinforce your goal by conditioning your environment so that you're constantly being reminded of it. By having these cues strategically placed where you can see and engage with them on a regular basis, you are sending a strong message of reinforcement that will help you act in line with your goal. These cues should be positive and encouraging.

Choose a photograph of yourself at your goal weight or size. If you don't have one, use a picture of the body you desire and put your head on it! Print out a couple of these photos and place them in strategic places throughout your home. Here are a few ideas of where you can place the photos for maximum effect:

your mirror or in a frame on your bedside table

inside your wardrobe door or on the front of your wardrobe, to remind you of how wonderful it will be when you can wear whatever you like!

on your fridge so that each time you go to eat something you are reminded of your goal: this will help provoke the question 'Am I hungry?'

as a screen saver on your phone and computer

in a frame: put it in your living room beside your TV, so that it's in your eyeline as you're watching

somewhere in your work space so that you can see it (if you'd rather it isn't visible to your colleagues, put it in your drawer so that each time you open it you can see it)

in your wallet, your car or anywhere that you will see it regularly (the image or the weight/measurements/dress size)

change all your passwords to your goal weight or measurements so that every time you type in your password you are sending yourself the message

of your goal (this is a really important one!)

By surrounding yourself with these conditioning cues you are constantly being reminded of your commitment. This will send a strong message to your brain, reminding you to act in line with this goal.

DECIDE THAT NOW IS THE TIME

What precedes all your actions around food? What determines the actions you take and therefore what your body becomes? What has brought you to this very point where you are unhappy with your body image?

The very simple answer is: decisions.

Every single thing you have put into your mouth, every unhelpful and unhealthy habit you have developed, has come from a decision, either conscious or unconscious. It is in the moments of decision that your body is shaped. It's true that some people are born with genetic and environmental advantages, yet we also know that we constantly meet, read and hear about people who have dramatically changed their body, so you know that it is absolutely possible. They just decided to experience a different way of inhabiting their body. If you decide to, you can have the body you want and truly deserve. Just by making a decision. You have set your goal; now decide to achieve it. If you don't make a decision about how you're going to be, then you have already made a decision to continue as you have been, carrying around the extra weight and feeling unhappy in your body.

LET GO OF ALL THE OLD BELIEFS ABOUT WEIGHT LOSS

When I was about thirteen, I stumbled across this quote ascribed to Socrates, 'Wisest is she who knows she does not know', in the book *Sophie's World*, which is a marvellous book at any age. Many years later, during my training as a psychoanalyst, I came again to understand the importance of allowing space for not knowing, and privileging that position. I think this is what has fuelled my appetite to grow and to never stop learning. I'm sharing this with you because I believe there is always space to grow and learn, and the best position from which to do this is one of understanding that we don't know. With this in mind, I have an important message to share with you:

Please do not think you know it all when it comes to losing weight.

When they first come to meet me, my clients always say the same thing: 'I know it all. I've tried everything and I know exactly what I should be doing, I just need some help with motivation.' But a position of certainty doesn't allow any space for lasting change. While I haven't come across this professionally, I'm sure you've all heard this trite adage: 'The definition of insanity is doing the same thing over and over again and expecting different results.' Well, doesn't this aptly fit with dieting?

Isn't it time you changed your beliefs around losing weight and allowed for the idea that you may not know it all? So many of my clients struggle to let go of their beliefs about weight loss. In fact, many of them tell me that they are weight-loss experts. I've worked with personal trainers, nutritionists and people who have read every diet book going and tried every diet, and think that they know it all.

Let me introduce you to a wonderful client, Deirdre, who was completely paralysed by her preconceived beliefs about weight loss. At forty-five, she had been fighting with her size ever since she became a mother in her mid twenties. Six feet tall and naturally gifted with a gorgeous slender body, she also had blonde hair, blue eyes and a wonderfully open smile. She was a naturally vivacious character and, before motherhood, she had been a model.

Because she was so statuesque, she had managed to carry quite a bit of extra weight before it became a significant issue for her. But with each child she gained more than a few pounds, and by the time she came to see me she was very unhappy with her body. Over the course of two decades she had tried every diet going, but nothing seemed to stick. In our first session she told me how she was a divorced mother of four, with a young baby and years and years worth of baggage holding her back from being the person she always thought she was going to be 'one day'. She was 30 or 40 lb overweight, unhappy in herself, and feeling like she was on a vicious roundabout that she couldn't get off.

What Deirdre and I discovered was that she felt the problem was simply genetic, as being overweight ran in her family. So, regardless of what she did to try and remedy the problem, she always believed that her attempts at weight loss would end in failure.

Through working together and helping her to dispel those entrenched myths around weight loss, Deirdre managed to completely change her beliefs and finally came to understand that she absolutely could return to a healthier size and a body that she enjoyed. She says:

> What I have learned most from Artful Eating is that the dieting I was doing for years was breaking me down mentally and physically. I needed to address the reasons I had needed to diet in the first place, and only in the realisation of the causes of my overeating could I continue with successful weight loss. I also needed to let go of the belief that I couldn't lose the weight because of my genes. I was convinced that my genetics determined my size. But I now get that it's these unhelpful beliefs that held me back from losing the weight.

In just over six months Deirdre lost 30 lb and changed her eating patterns completely without feeling deprived. For her, overcoming that mental block was absolutely central to her success.

So, now I have a rather big ask, but it is an essential one. If you don't truly commit to this, you will not get very far at all.

Let go of all of your preconceived ideas about how to lose weight.

This is an essential step. Call it a leap of faith if you like! But if you don't overcome and let go of the old beliefs, patterns and myths that you have accumulated over the years, you will continue to perpetuate the misguided behaviour that has led to your struggle with weight in the first place. In the long term, dieting hasn't worked, calorie counting hasn't worked, hitting the gym hasn't worked. There is so much misleading information propagated by big companies trying to sell their latest product that the truth has got lost. The obesity epidemic is a relatively new phenomenon. In the past we knew how to listen to our bodies and eat well; we were not cramming down artificial and 'low-fat' foods. Something has gone very wrong and it is time to rectify it.

Weight-loss myth #1:

People who are overweight have slower metabolic rates.

Truth: Studies comparing the resting energy expenditure of overweight people and lean people show little difference in basal metabolic rates. The ones that do demonstrate a difference show overweight people actually have higher metabolic rates. So it's time to let go of the idea that you just have a slow metabolism.[2]

WEIGHT-LOSS MYTH #2:
I must have the obesity gene.

Truth: Our genetics do not determine us. As I discussed in Chapter 1, half of the population have a version of FTO (the obesity gene) that contains one small change. These people are on average 3.3 lb heavier and 25 per cent more likely to become obese. Roughly one in six of us are unlucky enough to have two small changes, or a double-risk variant of FTO, and are on average 6.6 lb heavier and typically 50 per cent more likely to become obese. While people with these changes are less likely to feel satiated as quickly as those who do not have the variants that does not mean that they are fated to be overweight. There are many people who possess these variants who manage to maintain their desired weight and have learned to manage their hunger in a healthy way.

WEIGHT-LOSS MYTH #3:
I have to only eat diet food and I have to avoid all carbohydrates, sugars and fat.

Truth: Our body isn't designed to break down the artificial flavourings and sweeteners in so-called diet foods, so it is actually much better for us to eat and drink the real full-fat versions, such as real butter, milk and cheese. We are completely duped by food companies and labelling requirements that make us think a food is healthy. If the label says 'healthy choice', 'low in fat' or 'low in sugar', it must be good for you, right? What you should ask yourself is: what are they replacing the fat or the sugar with? The answer is artificial chemical products and flavourings that our body doesn't know how to metabolise and which ultimately make us sick and overweight.

WEIGHT-LOSS MYTH #4:
I have to do lots of cardiovascular exercise and I must do strenuous workouts at the gym, including lifting weights, to shift the fat.

Truth: This is also a complete myth. Exercise is very important for your mental well-being and for the health of your body, but studies show that it is not an efficient way to lose weight.[3]

WEIGHT-LOSS MYTH #5:
I have to count calories if I want to lose weight, and this is the only way I can lose weight.

Truth: Yes, counting calories and limiting your daily calorie intake will lead to weight loss. But let me ask you this: are you prepared to count calories for ever and control what you eat for ever? Honestly, how long can you stick to a strict regime, weighing out your food, avoiding eating out or at your friends' houses because you're trying to maintain that strict regime? As soon as you stop counting calories, the weight will pile back on. Also, not all calories are created equal. You can drink diet fizzy drinks all day long because they contain hardly any calories, but they wreak havoc on your body, your metabolism and your gut microbes. Eating these artificially developed low-calorie foods actually leads to weight gain, because they interfere with our body's natural way of breaking down and storing food.

Losing weight is difficult and I must deprive myself of the foods I love.

Truth: This is one of the main reasons diets don't work: they are unsustainable exactly because we have to eliminate so many of the things we enjoy eating. It makes it so difficult for us to eat out, go to a party, drink alcohol and just enjoy a healthy, balanced lifestyle. In Chapter 7 I will explain why it is actually a biological imperative to enjoy our food!

Far too many of you think you have all the right information on diet and weight loss, but you feel that there is something wrong with you because you can't lose the weight. Now is the time to recognise that the information is wrong, not you. We know, and have known for many decades, that diets don't work. If they did, you wouldn't be unhappy with your weight! We live in a society where we are desperate for quick fixes, in all aspects of our lives. We want the fastest, easiest route to the results we desire, and that is why so many of us have ended up on the yo-yo diet mill. So, are you finally ready to let go of the old, unhelpful beliefs? Wonderful: now you can begin to lose weight steadily and healthily and in a way that is easily maintainable, but also, most importantly, in a way that is enjoyable!

THE 48-HOUR KICK-STARTER CHALLENGE

'The pain you feel today is the strength you feel tomorrow. For every challenge encountered there is opportunity for growth.' Unknown

We have become far too used to oversized portions and eat way more than we need to nourish ourselves. This is a big problem and it is part of the reason that you have become unhappy with your body. Take a bit of time to think about how you eat and when you eat. Do you find that you wait until you're hungry to eat? Or do you eat simply because it is a mealtime, or because you have been offered something nice, or because you're bored, upset or peckish?

To kick-start the Artful Eating process, you need to lessen your appetite. In order to experience freedom with food, you simply must adjust to eating enough food to sustain you. I promise you this is the only 'challenging' thing I will ask you to do, and in fact many of my clients remark on how much they enjoy this process. When

we're fully grown, our stomach pretty much remains the same size, unless we intentionally have surgery to make it smaller. Eating less won't shrink your stomach, but it will help to reset your appetite so you won't feel as hungry.

Embarking on a new, more balanced lifestyle with the 48-hour Kick-starter lets you understand that you are committed to weight loss and to lasting change. This is a liquid-based mini-programme that will provide you with all the vitamins and minerals you need over a two-day period. It is a combination of vegetable juice and soup designed to make you feel great and mentally ready to completely change your relationship with and attitude to food. In a way, it is a marker that delineates the beginning of a new chapter in your life, one in which you have decided to take action and are committed to achieving your goal. It will also provide you with quick positive reinforcement, as you will most likely shed a few pounds.

We can become so rooted in our routine that it's hard to pull ourselves out. While this action may sound more like the initial stages of a traditional diet, do not feel anxious. These forty-eight hours will simply be a powerful kick-starter for a whole new way of being in which balance and equilibrium are effortlessly cultivated. It's all about attitude: how you approach the kick-starter will determine how you experience it, so have fun with this one and decide to do it at a time that works for you. Some people like to do it over a Saturday and Sunday, while others prefer to do it midweek, when they are busier and so more distracted. What is intended is that this will be the beginning of a lifelong commitment to balance and an appreciation for simple, unprocessed home-made produce packed with flavours and goodness. Every couple of months I like to do the kick-starter, as it clears the palate and can be a handy trick after a week of indulgence. Try it after you have completed the discovery week.

ACTION #1: THE 48-HOUR KICK-STARTER CHALLENGE

There is a lot to learn by undergoing this forty-eight-hour process. Start to practise body awareness over the two days: on an hourly basis, check in with yourself to see how hungry you actually are, and make a note of it.

Start with warm lemon water in the morning: Squeeze half a lemon into a large glass of warm water and drink it first thing before you eat or workout. Try adding freshly grated ginger or a little cayenne pepper for an added boost if you like.

I'm just going to pause right here and go on a little tangent to let you know how amazing this one simple action is. I not only recommend that you do this for your kick-starter, but I encourage you to do this *every single morning*. Lemons are absolutely amazing. They contain strong antibacterial, antiviral and immunity-boosting powers, and lemon juice is a digestive aid and liver cleanser, so it's great for weight loss. Lemons contain many substances, notably citric acid, calcium, magnesium, vitamin C, bioflavonoids, pectin and limonene, that promote immunity and fight infection. You should be using purified water and it should be lukewarm, not scalding hot. Ideally you should avoid ice-cold water, as it can be a lot for your body to process and it takes more energy to process ice-cold water than the warm. Always use fresh lemons, organic if possible, never bottled lemon juice. (Bonus tip: if your lemons are organic, zest them before you juice them. Keep a container in the freezer and just keep adding to it. Lemon zest is great to toss into pasta dishes, in salad dressings, cakes or biscuits.)

You can find all the below recipes in Chapter 12.

- breakfast: gorgeous green smoothie

- snack: vegetable juice or herbal tea – or, if you must, a cup of coffee or tea

- lunch: vegetable soup

- snack: gorgeous green smoothie

- dinner: vegetable soup

You should drink lots of water during the kick-starter (at least two litres a day), so feel free to enjoy herbal tea throughout the day and try some of the fabulous water infusions suggested below to help stave off hunger.

Follow this kick-starter menu for two days.

FLAVOURED-WATER IDEAS

Now I know not everyone likes the taste of water, so here are a few suggestions to mix it up! These simple ideas are a delicious alternative to fruit juices and fizzy drinks, which are so bad for us. Also, the flavoured waters look and taste fabulous!

Water and . . .

- sliced cucumber (my favourite!) – if you like, add a bit of peeled ginger to this

- fresh mint

- the juice of half a lemon or some lemon slices, or lime, or sliced watermelon (loaded with vitamins A and C)

- lime and basil (gives you a boost of vitamin C and iron)

- strawberries and a couple of basil leaves (vitamin C from the berries has been linked to fighting cancer and keeping wrinkles at bay, and basil boosts iron)

- raspberry and pineapple ice cubes (use frozen raspberries and pineapples in lieu of ice. Just pop the fruit in your ice-cube tray and fill with water. Indeed, you can do this with any fruit you like. This is also a good way of preserving fresh herbs for cooking.)

- orange and vanilla (if you don't have a vanilla bean or pod handy, you can substitute vanilla extract; both are naturally high in antioxidants)

- peach slices and cayenne pepper (may help curb appetite and promote calorie burn)

- blackberries and sage (blackberries are brimming with fibre and heart-healthy polyunsaturated fats, while sage contains vitamin A and a variety of minerals, like calcium and iron)

- *apples and cinnamon (combine a cinnamon stick, a pinch of ground cinnamon and some apple slices. Cinnamon helps lower blood sugar concentration and improves insulin sensitivity)*

- *blueberries, peach, lemon and mint (this supercharged mixture combines the antioxidant power of the fruit with refreshing mint, a carotene-rich aromatic herb. Like a yummy sangria, without the alcohol!)*

Let your chosen accompaniments infuse in the filtered water for at least fifteen minutes, and then enjoy the subtle flavours.

HOME-MADE TEA INFUSIONS

Tea infusions are lovely any time of day, and I really enjoy making them when friends come to call because they look beautiful, feel special and taste delicious. Creating your own home custom tea is really simple and enjoyable. Get creative with flavours you enjoy. Anything goes, really! During the kick-starter a tea infusion can be very comforting and it is a much better alternative to black tea or coffee. Here are some flavour ideas:

- *lemon and lemongrass (a very refreshing tea)*

- *apple, ginger and thyme (gives a beautifully full-bodied flavour)*

- *peppermint (a simple classic and my favourite)*

- *lemon, ginger and half a teaspoon of turmeric (as Donovan would say, 'mellow yellow'!)*

If you have a French press, use this. If not, you can put the ingredients in a muslin bag or just straight into your pot. Add boiling water and let them infuse for about five to ten minutes. Pour into a lovely teacup and enjoy!

 ## ACTION #2: REFLECTIONS AND REALISATIONS (10 MINUTES)

Enjoy the process and answer the following:

- *How does your body and mind react to the drastic change in diet?*

- *How do you experience hunger? Where do you feel it?*

- *How does your mind respond to hunger? What are you thinking?*

- *How strong is your resolve to stick to the forty-eight-hour programme?*

- *Did you find you gave in at any point? If so, what thoughts,*

feelings and sensations did you experience before you gave in? And then after you gave in?

Anything else you noticed, physically, mentally and emotionally?

Over the course of the kick-starter you will lose some weight. Most likely this will be water, but the aim is to mentally prepare your mind for change. You are letting yourself know that you are about to embark on a whole new way of eating and experiencing food. The tastes you will experience over these two days are adventurous for some palates, though I think you'll have a hard time feeling like you are massively depriving yourself, especially if the tastes are new to you. If you do give in and eat something that isn't on the menu, that's okay, do not beat yourself up. Simply return to the menu for the remainder of the duration. Do your best: that is all you can ask of yourself, so be kind and enjoy the process, however rigidly you stick to it.

5

FOOD AND HOME REBOOT

'The food you eat can either be the safest and most powerful form of medicine or the slowest form of poison.' Ann Wigmore

In this chapter you will:
discover what to eat and, more importantly, what not to eat
understand why it is essential to eradicate processed foods from your diet
discover the joys of decluttering, to prepare your environment for a new, healthier, more enjoyable lifestyle.

The most important ingredient of experiencing freedom with food is recognising that food is delicious fuel. What we eat is nourishing our body and our brain. We have disengaged so much from this fact and it has led to an objectification of our bodies in a very unhealthy way. It's time to start enjoying food. The only elimination I encourage is eliminating guilt! Once you begin to enjoy food, things will start to change in a very exciting way.

So far you have learned about the psychology and physiology that underpins weight loss. You have set a goal and taken decisive action. How do you find the 48-hour Kick-starter? Did you enjoy it? Did you find that after the first day you weren't that hungry? Did you lose a couple of pounds? If you did, that's an encouraging start, if you didn't, do not worry: our bodies take time to adjust and the weight will start to fall away, have faith! Remember Newton's third law of motion:

For every action, there is an equal and opposite reaction.

You have taken action and started to question your relationship with food and your body. This is a powerful shift in your position.

It is time now to establish what to eat. While there is no need to prohibit or curtail any major food group, it's time to seriously assess what we are eating and how it is affecting our size and health. When we eat an apple, our body is able to recognise and digest it easily: it distributes the nutrients and actually engages your metabolism. However, when we drink apple juice made from concentrate, our body gets confused as it tries to identify the artificial ingredients. When your digestive system can't identify a food substance, it isn't broken down, so instead it is stored as fat, in an effort to keep it away from your vital organs. On the whole, these highly processed foods have little or no nutritional value and, ultimately, make you fat.

Let me be very clear here: the enemy isn't sugar, it isn't fat, it isn't carbohydrates . . . It's overly processed food. All of the so-called healthy 'diet foods' and processed foods are actually extremely bad for us. They are a massive part of why in the West we are suffering from an obesity epidemic. The most significant influence you have over your health is in what you eat, and this has nothing to do with calories, as all calories are not created equal. With each bite you take, your brain receives instructions that change your biology, altering your gene expression. Depending on what you eat, you are turning on the 'fat genes' or the 'skinny genes', the healthy or disease genes. This information also controls your immune system and even turns on and off inflammation depending on what you eat. Calories high in sugar and starch actually slow down your metabolism, whereas calories higher in fat speed it up, so it is crucial to understand that foods cannot be reduced to their calorific value.[1]

Instead, think of the food you eat as information that affects your hormones, insulin levels, thyroid, blood sugar, sex hormones, adrenal hormones and so on. All of these things are influenced with every bite of food you eat. What is fascinating and encouraging is that these changes don't occur over time; they actually happen minute by minute. By eliminating overly processed foods from your diet, you will significantly improve your biological make-up in a very short space of time!

There is a further troubling side effect of this relatively new phenomenon of a highly processed diet that has crept into the mainstream. Recent research has opened up our understanding about why we are getting bigger, and it indicates that the obesity epidemic is due in great part to the fact that what we are eating has massively changed.[2] As we can see, our bodies are not used to all of the artificial and overly processed foods that now make up the majority of our diet. These hostile ingredients also diminish the gut's natural microbes, which are essential for our health and for maintaining a healthy weight. New research has shown that a limited variety of gut microbes correlates with obesity, so it is important that we eat food that isn't full of all sorts of manufactured chemicals, preservatives, flavourings and additives.

I hope this information will empower you and reinforce your conviction to eradicate processed foods from your diet. If you're tired, find it difficult to concentrate, have skin issues or poor-quality nails and hair then eradicating processed foods will very quickly help to rectify these issues from the inside out. We are constantly looking for pills and miracle potions to fix us, but what we don't realise is how close we are to health and well-being. Research has shown that eating a diet rich in fresh non-processed foods can reverse type 2 diabetes, eliminate chronic migraines, help improve bowel issues, asthma issues and so on. These truly are compelling findings![3]

Unfortunately, our modern environment facilitates negative eating behaviours. It is much easier to find a convenience shop filled with pre-prepared and overly processed foods than to find fresh non-processed foods adorning the shelves. What frustrates me is that the foods on offer seem healthy, but they typically aren't. It is challenging for us to eat well when the labelling and presentation of food can be so misleading.[4]

What is really concerning about the struggle to avoid unhealthy foods is that so many people think they are eating well and being healthy, but really they are being duped by false and misleading advertising. When we turn to 'diet foods' or 'healthy-food' products that boast of being low in fat, we have to ask ourselves, 'What are these fats being replaced with?' Often the answer is hidden sugars. So let us hold a magnifying glass over this one aspect of these so-called 'healthy foods' and explore the prevalence of hidden sugars.

We know that foods contain natural sugars, but the food industry regularly replaces 'fat content' with hidden sugars to make diet foods, which are wreaking havoc on our bodies. In the West, people are developing type 2 diabetes, our teeth are suffering, and this excess sugar is a direct cause of the weight we are gaining and struggling to lose. Unwittingly we fill our cupboards with food-like substances, low-fat salad dressing for example, comprising things such as high-fructose corn syrup, trans fats and monosodium glutamate.

The UK government's Scientific Advisory Committee on Nutrition (SACN) provides a recommended daily allowance of seven teaspoons of free sugars per day. This does not include the natural sugars found in food. Let me differentiate here: free sugars are the sugars added to food and drink, as well as sugar found naturally in honey, syrups, fruit juices and fruit juice concentrates, unlike naturally occurring sugars, which can be found in fruit and milk. The major problem is these free sugars, the sugar added to processed foods that we don't realise we are ingesting. Let's take a look at what you might well think is a healthy-eating plan for a day, to illustrate the dangers of processed foods:

🌿 *Breakfast: A regular-size bowl of bran flakes, milk, two tablespoons of low-fat yogurt and berries, and a glass of orange juice from a carton. 14 teaspoons*

🌿 *Lunch: Cream of tomato soup and two slices of wholegrain bread. 3 teaspoons*

🌿 *Afternoon snack: Flavoured water and granola bar. 9 teaspoons*

🌿 *Dinner: Prawn stir-fry, with peppers, leafy greens and a jar of lemon and ginger stir-fry sauce. (One portion of the sauce has ten teaspoons of free sugars!) 10 teaspoons*

This 'healthy' meal plan resulted in you consuming thirty-six teaspoons of hidden sugars, over five times the recommended daily amount. You are starting your day with double the recommended daily allowance of sugar, and by the time you have had your afternoon snack you have ingested twenty-six teaspoons of sugar![5]

I love this quote by Ann Wigmore, an early whole-food champion born at the turn of the last century, who summed it up perfectly: 'The food you eat can either be the safest and most powerful form of medicine or the slowest form of poison.'

Now, you may think that you don't eat a lot of processed foods. But food labelling and our idea of what processed foods are is so out of synch with the reality.[6] Return to your food journal from Chapter 1. Did you have pasta with a ready-made sauce? Did you have fish, meat or chicken that was prepared in some sort of flavouring or shop-bought sauce? Did you have low-fat yogurt, fruit juice, margarine, ham, bacon, veggie burgers, soya or tofu, breakfast cereal, mass-produced cheese, ready-made salad dressing, sliced bread, crackers, overly processed jams and preserves, poor-quality tomato ketchup, chips (even oven chips), ready-made salads, coleslaw, egg-mayonnaise, a ready-made meal and so on? All of the above contain unnatural chemicals and flavourings, which are directly related to you being overweight and staying overweight. These additives are making your fat cells larger and as a result you are getting fatter. Are you starting to get the idea? Once we have identified what is not good for us to eat and, more importantly, why it is not good for us, it's time to get clear on what types of foods you should nourish your body with.

Stick to my very simple rule: If you can't pronounce it or don't recognise it, do not eat it!

I can sense that you might be starting to get a bit worried, panicked even. Don't be: I promise that you can experience freedom with food as

long as it is good, whole food. What I mean by whole food is food that has not been heavily processed.

Now, a little note to those people who don't enjoy vegetables or fruit: you will learn to love them! Because so many of our fruits and vegetables are force-grown and full of chemicals and pesticides, they just don't taste very nice. Switch over to organic and you will taste the wonderful difference. Also, at the end of the book I have included delicious, easy recipes that will change your attitude to fruit and vegetables. I have worked with so many people who have told me they don't like vegetables, but once they started experimenting with food and flavours (something we will explore in Chapter 10) their taste buds began to develop a sophistication and desire for healthy food. I understand that encouraging you to purposefully eradicate processed food from your diet is challenging, and I recognise on the surface that it is easier said than done. So now I am going to introduce you to some fascinating research that will help you eradicate those old unhealthy and unhelpful food habits and create space for new, healthier approaches to only eating the good stuff.

WHAT CHANGES CAN YOU MAKE IN YOUR HOME TO SET YOU UP FOR SUCCESS?

Professor Brian Wansink conducted interesting research on the psychology of food. Wansink found that he could pretty much predict how much people were going to weigh based on what food was immediately visible to the eye in their homes.[7]

For instance, if you have crisps or biscuits on display, you will weigh 8–11 lb more than the family who doesn't, and you'll be 22 lb heavier if you have soft drinks visible in the house. The worst culprit is breakfast cereal, which we would generally think of as good for us, as it's advertised as being high in fibre and fortified with vitamins and iron, but it's actually highly processed. Having it visible in your kitchen means you are on average about 20 lb heavier than a person who doesn't. Conversely, if you have fruit on display, you are likely to weigh 8.8 lb less than the person who doesn't, so it's time to start filling that fruit bowl! People with toasters on their counter will weigh about 9 lb more than a person who doesn't display their toaster, and if you have a blender on show, you are more likely to weigh less. So have a look around your kitchen and see what foods and appliances are influencing your eating habits positively and negatively. On average we make 250 decisions about food every day, so we want to encourage easy, positive food choices.

ACTION #1: DETOX YOUR KITCHEN (1 DAY)

'A place for everything and everything in its place': with this compelling information in mind, it's time to declutter your kitchen and your home. Our kitchens, and indeed most of our homes, can become a dumping ground for unnecessary and useless items that we

struggle to let go of. It's important to declutter your home. This is a symbolic act that reflects the transformation your mind and body will experience as you embark on reprogramming to the Artful Eating way of life. Clearing out your cupboards and reorganising your kitchen will not only set you up for success by eliminating any unhelpful and unnecessary foods, but it will also mark a new chapter in your life.

Having an organised, clean, inviting kitchen full of flavoursome healthy foods will help reinforce the wonderful changes you are making mentally and physically. Having an inviting, clean space where everything you need to prepare and cook is easily accessible is also essential. It's time to do away with all the unhealthy, overly processed foods, so block off some time and assess your fridge and cupboards.

1. START WITH ALL THE FOODSTUFFS IN YOUR CUPBOARDS AND FRIDGE

Pull everything out and lay it on your kitchen table so that you can see what you have. Give away:

- *anything with ingredients you can't pronounce*

- *anything supposedly fresh but with a long shelf life*

- *all processed meats (ham/salami/ prosciutto/sausage/chorizo/ bacon). If you love these (like I*

do) then they should be enjoyed as an occasional treat, not part of your daily diet

- *all overly processed food: breakfast cereals, salad dressings, sauces (pasta, curry etc.), snacks, ready meals, pre-prepared foods, frozen snacks, sliced bread (brown or white), granola bars, snack bars, microwave butter popcorn, crisps, and frozen flavoured foodstuffs like chicken goujons, lemon fish, and crackers with lots of strange ingredients*

- *fruit juices, fizzy drinks (diet or full fat), cordials, flavoured waters*

- *anything pre-prepared: ready-made dinners, desserts, soups, sauces*

- *anything with too many ingredients to count*

Remember, if you can't pronounce it or don't recognise it – don't eat it.

Once you have established the foods you are keeping, group them on the table according to food type and usage. Group tinned foods together, dairy together, brans and pulses together, herbs and spices together and baking ingredients together, and so on.

2. GET ACQUAINTED WITH THE BASICS

I have provided a list of basic store cupboard ingredients in Chapter 12; these will be all you need to get started cooking and experimenting in the kitchen. The great thing about this list is that most things won't go off for a very long time, so you can stock up and replenish as and when you need it. These ingredients will help turn any basic meal into something really delicious.

Tinned and frozen produce are fantastic as they maintain their goodness without the need for preservatives. Frozen produce is picked in its prime and preserved in that condition until you need to use it, so has great nutritional value. If you don't have everything on the list, go out and get it! I recommend that you always have these basic ingredients to hand, then buy your fresh produce as and when you need it.

One of the basic Artful Eating principles is to use the best quality you can afford and try to use organic whenever possible. Your taste buds and your body will thank you.

3. REORGANISE YOUR KITCHEN SO THAT EVERYTHING IS EASILY ACCESSIBLE AND VISIBLE

Next, clear out your non-food cupboards and lay everything on an old sheet on the floor. As you clear each cupboard, group like items on the sheet. This will help you to decide what to keep and what to discard.

Now that you have emptied everything out, use this opportunity to give your kitchen a really deep clean.

Returning to your items, consider what to keep. Try and be ruthless: only keep things you need, use and enjoy. This will free up space so that you can easily see what you have at a glance upon opening a cupboard or drawer.

As a guide, in Chapter 12 you'll find a list of the basic kitchen utensils I recommend. Invest in the best quality you can afford, as good-quality utensils make for a much easier life when cooking or baking, and they should last a lifetime. This is a long list, so take your time to acquire all the items.

Don't save your 'good things' for special occasions; use and enjoy them! I was gifted a beautiful Royal Stafford china tea set by my mother. It's a traditional fine bone white and gold set with beautiful delicately painted pink roses. I adore it and enjoy drinking coffee out of it every day. I have to say that drinks taste better from this set than from a normal mug. Friends often comment on the difference in taste! If you have lovely things, use and enjoy them, don't let them sit gathering dust.

Either discard or donate duplicate items, or anything that isn't frequently used, or anything that is broken or missing a part.

Once you have streamlined the content of your kitchen to things you love, need and actually use, it's time to consider how to store your items in a way that works for you and the flow of your kitchen:

- *Try to keep similar items together, or group by types of foods. I keep baking ingredients, pulses, beans and dried foods together, and tinned and preserved foods together.*

- *Likewise, group together: cooking items; plates and tableware; glassware and cups; utensils; and dishes for entertaining and seasonal items*

- *Store cooking and baking items close to where you do food preparation.*

- *Utensils should be in the drawer nearest to the food-preparation area.*

- *You could place glassware near the sink or fridge.*

- *Find a suitable counter space, ideally near your tap, for a coffee or tea station that includes cups and filters.*

- *With food, I use containers inside my cabinets. They are clearly labelled and keep things fresh. It makes it so much easier to see what I have and keeps everything clean.*

- *I also love to display my foods and utensils. My husband made a very simple shallow open shelf where I keep all my condiments, herbs, sauces, oils, jams and spices. I can see everything easily and I constantly get compliments about it.*

- *Consider using wall space or a ceiling rack to hang pots and pans. Keep in mind that any space you can use to hang something will free up flat space inside a cabinet, and it also makes it easy to see what you need and easy to use things.*

The idea is to make your kitchen an inviting and easy-to-manage space where you know what you have and where everything is. Your own personal style will determine where you store and how you use the items.

Take the time and energy to declutter and organise your kitchen. It is an investment that will pay off in happiness and will make for an enjoyable environment where you like spending time. This will be very important later on when I teach you how to get creative cooking in the kitchen. Once you have cleared out your kitchen, you will feel fantastic! As with the 48-hour Kick-starter, this action will have a deep mental-cleansing effect as you prepare your space for a life that is balanced and enjoyable.

A few years ago my husband was giving lectures on international development to secondary schools around the country. I remember him talking about two schools in particular that he visited on the same day. They were in the same district; in fact, they were only a couple of kilometres apart. One school was in prefabricated buildings: it was old, grotty, and badly heated. The other was a new, state-of-the-art space lovingly designed for learning. It was bright, spacious and functioned perfectly. Liam couldn't get over the difference in demeanour of the two sets of students. The students in the grotty building lacked respect, looked dishevelled, did not participate well, and were boisterous and challenging, while the students in the new building were respectful, well presented, calm and engaging. Liam's observation really struck me, as both sets of students where from the same socio-economic background and both schools were state-run. It is clear that our environment has a huge determination over how we feel and act. So this piece of the Artful Eating puzzle is essential. Make your home an inviting, clean, organised and beautiful place to be and positive behaviours will follow!

I absolutely adore coming home. I always have fresh-cut flowers and lots of beautiful houseplants, my walls are filled with art from my travels, and I have an eclectic mix of furniture, lovingly collected over the years. My home is my sanctuary; I only allow space for things I love, use and enjoy. When I'm at home I feel peaceful, comfortable and happy. This is the feeling I want for you too, as feeling good is essential. Life can get in the way and we can experience stressful times, so it is important that we make the effort to have the basics right: a kitchen full of good, wholesome foods; a home that is clean, organised, comfortable and inviting; and a bedroom and wardrobe filled with things we enjoy wearing that make us feel good and look our best! Having recently started a family, I get how challenging it can be to keep one's home clean and tidy. This is why having an organised home is so essential. When everything has a specific place, it is much easier to keep things clean and tidy.

ACTION #2: DECLUTTER YOUR BEDROOM AND WARDROBE (1 DAY)

Artful Eating is all about enjoying the good things in life. When we treat ourselves and our things with respect, we look and feel wonderful. If you have a messy, disorganised dressing space filled with things that don't fit, or just 'comfy clothes', then you are sending a powerful message to yourself, reinforcing a lack of self-respect. It's important that you take pride in your appearance, as it will help you feel more confident and motivated to achieve your goal. You are preparing to slim down and in the process it's important that you feel good in your skin every single day. Preparing your home for this will make the change more manageable.

It's very easy to give up and not be in tune with your goals if you're constantly wearing loose-fitting comfy clothing that hides your figure. This is a big problem!

Your dressing space and wardrobe should be as organised and easy to navigate as your newly revolutionised kitchen. When our closet is overcrowded, it's very difficult to see what we actually have, so free up space, literally and mentally, and privilege well-made, flattering items. Having everything neatly in order will be invaluable when you are getting dressed. If you feel like you look good, you will act accordingly and walk with grace and confidence, and, importantly, you will find that you no longer overindulge because you are unhappy with how you look.

ORGANISE YOUR WARDROBE

As you did with your kitchen, and as challenging as it sounds, it's time to really see what's going on behind closed doors. Decluttering makes things simpler and it also reflects what I want you to do with your shopping list: choose quality over quantity.

- *Pull everything out. This can actually be quite enjoyable, as you rediscover things that you forgot you had.*

- *Keep and use only the best items, and let go of the things don't deserve to take up space.*

- *If items are old, shabby, ill-fitting and over-worn then it's time to throw them out.*

- *Donate anything that you have duplicates of (remember, quality over quantity here).*

- *This goes for underwear and sleep attire also: only hold on to the very best, things that fit well, look good on you and make you feel good.*

- *Personally, I organise my wardrobe according to colour, hanging similar-coloured clothes together. It certainly looks pleasing to the eye and makes it very easy to find what I'm looking for.*

Do not worry if you feel that you have nothing left! You are much better off with a slimmed-down wardrobe that you can thoughtfully and consciously add to than a closet bursting with unflattering and worn-out clothing.

- *Be mindful about how you store your clothing.*

- *Take time to lovingly and respectfully fold and store your clothes.*

- *Hang what is necessary and fold what lends itself well to folding. Store folded things vertically so*

that you can instantly see what you have, instead of having to rummage through deep drawers.

- *Ideally you should be able to see everything at a glance.*

- *With this in mind, shoeboxes are excellent to place in drawers and are handy drawer dividers, which allow for vertical storage.*

- *Fold your socks, tights and underwear vertically in shoeboxes so that you can instantly see and easily access them.*

- *It is much better to have a small number of good-quality socks and tights, as they won't run as easily, will last longer and will feel really good each time you put them on.*

- *Have a decent full-length mirror and good lighting. When you are dressing and doing your make-up, you need to be able to see, so ensure the light is flattering. Natural light works best.*

What you are cultivating is a sense of pride in your appearance and your home and the objects you populate it with. Begin today: take care of your hair and nails. If you've worn the same make-up for years, go into a decent make-up counter and get some advice. The staff will do your make-up for you so that they can advertise their products, and you can buy one or two products if you wish. As you did with your wardrobe, throw out any old make-up and beauty products you don't use or need. Streamlining the products you use and choosing quality over quantity lets you know you value yourself. Treat yourself with care, respect and love. Don't save your favourite perfume or jewellery for special occasions; life is happening right now, so embrace and privilege every day. You must take pride in your appearance now, not when you have lost the weight.

In all things I want you to focus on feeling good now: this will absolutely help you to achieve your goal, as you will feel motivated, committed and confident.

ARTFUL EATING

MAIN COURSE

MENTAL
REPROGRAMMING

'Don't limit yourself. Many people limit themselves to what they think they can do.
You can go as far as your mind lets you. What you believe, remember, you can achieve.'
Mary Kay Ash

In this chapter you will:
deeply assess your own personal story, the beliefs and limiting thoughts that have
shaped your body and behaviour
create a new story which you will carry with you going forward, a story that allows you
to feel empowered about having the body and healthy life you truly desire
mentally prepare yourself for change
leverage your commitment to change.

At this point you are probably feeling enthusiastic about committing to the Artful Eating philosophy. I know that you want this to work and I do too, I really want that for you. But you've been here before, right? So it is extremely important that this enthusiasm and commitment lasts and that you do not find yourself in a couple of weeks, or months, feeling frustrated, despondent and not following through. That's why this chapter is so important. It's all about lasting change and I have created a cognitive hypnosis audio to help you maintain your commitment and embrace this new way of being. To access it, go to www.artful-eating.com.

The story we tell ourselves shapes us, inside and out. Every action we take is deeply influenced by how we view ourselves, and this has been directly shaped by our upbringing and our relationships – initially with our parents and siblings, and then with those who we interact with throughout our lives. It's time to discover what your own personal story is. In doing this, you will be able to explore more deeply the conscious and unconscious blocks to permanent and lasting weight loss.

I had a wonderful client, Mary, who from a very young age was nicknamed 'Bin' because she would eat anything she was fed and she would even eat everyone's leftovers too! She enjoyed food, was encouraged to eat as much as she liked, and had no sense of feeling self-conscious about her eating habits. Mary was skinny throughout childhood and adolescence. Her weight just wasn't an issue; her story was simply that she loved food and had a healthy appetite.

When she was about twenty-one she hurt her back doing a water-sports knockout competition. The doctor who examined her showed her the X-ray of her back, tracing the outline of her spine and saying that it was 'perfect'. He then traced the curve of the outline of her stomach with his finger, over a little tiny round mound of lightness on the X-ray and said, 'And look, that's your tummy, you're getting a bit plump!'

From this one, thoughtless sentence, everything changed.

She explained to me that it wasn't exactly what he had said; it was how he said it. She felt objectified, and in that moment, something shifted. Her nickname had never had a negative connotation for her; she was just a girl who loved her food. But being seen in this way by the doctor made her suddenly very self-conscious. What ensued were forty years of yo-yo dieting. She immediately went on a diet, joined a gym and began a health and fitness regime in an effort to attain the 'perfect' measurements and weight. In her twenties she got a personal trainer, did lots of weights and worked out all the time. She remembered how during that time she was really skinny, but as soon as she stopped the gruelling routine she regained all the weight she lost, and more. Her weight and size became a major preoccupation, whereas in the past she hadn't given it a thought. Mary told me how throughout her adult life she was constantly trying the latest fad diet or diet pill, tea, or weight-loss club memberships, but nothing stuck.

Mary's story had changed. It had shifted from being a happy, healthy young woman whose story was 'I eat what I like and I have a great body' to 'I don't like my body and it's a constant struggle and a challenge to have the body I desire'.

Over the years Mary eventually lost her drive to keep dieting and she found herself putting on more and more weight. Her story then became 'I am the "fat friend" of the group and I can never wear the clothes I like'. Food became a huge issue for her. She would overindulge and then feel guilty for it. As she became more unhappy with her body, her self-esteem plummeted. Food then became a big source of guilt as she overindulged to make herself feel better because she was so unhappy with how she looked. She was in a vicious circle that she couldn't pull herself out of. By the time she came to see me she was exhausted, fed up, and very overweight and disillusioned. Worst of all, she felt like she knew it all. Because she really had tried everything.

Once she shared her story with me, she began to see how it had shaped her life and her body. By encouraging Mary to reflect on her body and her food story, I helped her to see how the story we tell ourselves informs every single decision we make and ultimately shapes the person we are, inside and out. You've seen this in action yourself, right? You have a colleague or friend who always wins things or who always seems to get what they want. *This is because that is their story.*

So together Mary and I did a lot of work on shifting her beliefs about her weight and the story she had been living. We looked back over her life and recognised the very point where things went wrong. This is when I found out about that moment with the doctor. I asked her to forgive herself, the doctor, or anyone who had made a comment about her body in the past, and simply let go of all the past negative thoughts and beliefs she had about her body. I encouraged Mary to consciously change her story to 'I have a beautiful body that I love and respect, and I effortlessly and easily achieve the body I desire and deserve'.

This one shift in perspective unblocked all the limiting beliefs that had prevented Mary from achieving a weight she was happy with in the past. Addressing these issues at a conscious level can be incredibly emancipating; however, we do inevitably have unconscious, deep-seated beliefs that affect us. Over the space of three months Mary lost 22 lb and actually enjoyed the process! It is essential that you experience this shift too, as it is most certainly one of the major blocks to achieving and, most importantly, maintaining your goal.

ACTION #1: DISCOVER YOUR STORY (60 MINUTES, BUT PERHAPS A COUPLE OF DAYS' CONTEMPLATION FIRST)

Mary uncovered and became conscious of her story, and through this awareness she was able to consciously rewrite it. This change helped her shift from being in a position of trying to lose weight to being in a position of effortlessly losing it and achieving the body she desired!

1. START TO THINK ABOUT YOUR OWN STORY

Take some time and space and really think about your weight and life story. Try your best

to be honest with yourself. I know that we cannot purposefully become aware of what is unconsciously shaping us, but there are plenty of conscious experiences, memories and beliefs that we can access.

Start by brainstorming all the words and thoughts that come to your mind about you, your body, your weight and the type of person you see yourself as.

Next, write out answers to these questions. Ideally you want to allow your thoughts to flow, so don't think too hard; just begin to write and see what emerges. Your answers should be as detailed as possible, maybe even a couple of paragraphs (or more!) each. Include memories, feelings, experiences and people who contributed to these feelings about your body. This is an opportunity for you to untangle some of the entrenched beliefs that have been inhibiting your ability to achieve your goal, so privilege this exercise.

WHEN DO YOU FIRST REMEMBER BEING UNHAPPY WITH YOUR BODY?

ARE/WERE THERE OTHER PEOPLE IN YOUR FAMILY WHO WERE UNHAPPY WITH THEIR WEIGHT?

WHEN DID YOU FIRST START DIETING?

Was there ever a time when you were happy with your body?

What have other people said about your appearance?

What do you feel about your body now?

This is a really challenging exercise and I want you to open up and invest the time and energy to explore your thoughts. You may want to record your story and listen back to it, if that works better for you than writing it down.

Once you have done that, look and see what words, thoughts and ideas emerge. How negative are they when it comes to food, weight loss and your body? Can you see a story emerging?

Now, take the time to write a page that encapsulates this story. Read it. Feel it. You may have an emotional response to it. My clients typically have a very strong emotional response to this exercise, and that's a good thing. So if you feel the need to cry, please do. Let it out. Talk it out with a loved one or trusted friend if you feel you can or would like to. And indeed, if you realise that what has emerged is overwhelming, then I encourage you to go and speak to a therapist (please see the end of the book for advice on finding a therapist).

By unearthing, acknowledging and feeling your story, you are working on letting it go. My clients often find it hard to face their story, and you may too, as you have been living it for so many years.

I hope that by doing this exercise you now realise how much it has been holding you back. But facing your story is also empowering, as gaining this insight into your thoughts and beliefs will allow you to start to address and change them.

It is challenging to change one's story, especially because it seems that we are hard-wired to repeat that which is familiar to us and also because there are deep-seated unconscious thoughts at play that we cannot access without professional help. But the one, very powerful thing you can do is consciously create a new story for yourself, one that is in line with the very best version of who you can be and what your goal is.

This new story is one in which you love your body now and you respect it.

You understand and want to nourish it.

You find it effortless and easy to lose weight, and you are enjoying achieving your weight-loss goal as you shed the unnecessary and unhealthy weight you have been carrying around.

As you shift into the position of this new story, you enjoy the good feelings and confidence that comes with it.

You're happier and healthier and so it is much easier for you to lose weight and keep it off.

You may want to share your thoughts with your family and friends. How do they see you? It may be different to how you view yourself. Really challenge yourself to address this now, as it is the most important piece of the Artful Eating puzzle. If you don't commit to being open and honest with yourself, real lasting change just can't happen. I am so excited for this new chapter in your life where you let go of the old story and make way for a new, positive one where you love yourself and your body!

2. WRITE OUT YOUR NEW STORY ON A PAGE NOW

Take your time to craft it lovingly. Fill it with all the hope, kindness and love that you deserve. Within this page is the blueprint of your best version of you and it will help carry you forward in a more intentional way, where your story is in line with who you are now. By creating a new story, you are forging the space and focus to truly change your beliefs and behaviours for life.

Read your new story every morning and evening while you are in the process of realignment, the period where you are moving towards your goal weight, and continue to do it once you have achieved your goal. You could even record the new story on your phone and listen back to it every morning and evening. This is a powerful exercise, so privilege it. While you are engaging with your new story, really feel it, believe it, allow lovely warm feelings of positivity to flow through you as you read it. If you find that developing a conscious awareness of your story and the practice of rewriting and embracing a new one fails to shift your position, then I encourage you to speak with a therapist who will guide you as you untangle these negative beliefs.

A fantastic client of mine has graciously let me share her before-and-after story, to give you a sense of what I'm talking about. These two paragraphs are the distillation of a lot of journalling and work, so be aware that they are the end product! I love the insight and contrast between these two pictures of herself:

The weight story I have been living for so many years:

I live in denial of being overweight, until I see myself in a photo, a window, or on Facetime/ Skype, etc. Then it's like I have been struck in the face, I'm so shocked at the woman I see there. I'm ashamed, and sometimes that shame cycles down into imagining what everyone has been thinking, while I have been living in denial. In the past, I attacked this shame by going on very strict diets, in one case losing up to three stone over less than a year. Shame kept that weight off for a while. But counteracting that is the shame of having to eat differently than everyone else in public (thus calling attention to my weight). On enough occasions, the fact that my extreme diet had to be catered for when I stayed at friends' houses caused me so much embarrassment that I gave up the diet that had been 'successful' and reverted to trying to have some kind of self-control to maintain the weight loss. It has never worked. I have steadily gained weight over the years. In fact I have gained six stone since I first arrived in Ireland (feeling fat!). Now in my journey, I am working very hard at separating the need for healthy eating from the societal obsession with having a skinny body shape. Valuing body shape so intently produces a never-satiated monster. It's contrary to the value of inner character and beauty that I pretend I believe in. I have chronic fatigue/ME and my energy is limited. Being overweight means I create a lot more work for myself doing everyday tasks. I find myself unable to take part in some activities with my younger friends, and that is sad. I have trouble believing there is a way out of this quandary.

My new weight story:

(Fair warning: Because I am a Christ-follower, my new story involves him.) In my new weight story, weight is not preoccupying my mind and emotions, even unconsciously, nor am I living in denial of being overweight. Seeing myself in a picture reminds me of the fun I had being with my friends instead of how I looked at the time. I do not weigh myself, and if I feel my clothes are tight, it doesn't launch me into despair. My choices are based on the food I enjoy, being free to eat what tastes good, albeit a little at a time. I notice hunger, and that signals me to eat, rather than boredom or a desire for something to do. I am able to pass up eating a whole cake, a whole pie or a full tub of ice cream because I focus on the enjoyable bit I had and I don't need to eat those things just because they are there. At that point I am no longer hungry, which enables me to leave some nice things to eat for the next time. I have energy and freedom of movement, insofar as having less weight to carry around enables me to. I have a list of creative things to do when I feel too tired to go out, other than eat. I live in conformity to my own values, which are that a rich spiritual life, good peer relationships, and having a diverse set of people to love and serve make a valuable life. My physical body is important, because it is the means of relating to people and to nature. It's for me to be grateful to have a body to live in, in this world, rather than to compare mine with everyone else's. My new story incorporates those things into my journey, where my core beliefs would drop down deep into my soul. In this new freedom, my mom's anxieties and insecurities about her level of attractiveness are no longer mirrored in my own heart. My compassion for her results in my resolve not to repeat her behaviour, but to be free of those shackles. Amen.

DESTROY LIMITING BELIEFS

This next exercise is really a continuation of the story exercise. By creating a new story you are destroying the limiting beliefs that have shaped your life. I'm sure we all know smokers who went through this same shift from belief to conviction. Most people want to quit smoking, but usually it takes more than willpower to stop: there must be conviction. You'll often hear of people who smoked for many, many years and just one day decided to quit. Something triggers a shift from the belief that it would be a good idea to quit to an unbreakable conviction.

ACTION #2: ERADICATE LIMITING THOUGHTS (20 MINUTES)

A) Mark out of ten how firmly you believe these statements to be true for you (1 being not at all true, 10 being complete conviction).

- *I can do it.*
- *I am destined to have a beautiful healthy body.*
- *I love my body.*
- *I lose weight effortlessly and easily.*
- *I feel pleasure as I don't finish my portion or push the plate away with food still on it.*
- *I have a new story which shapes my body and life in a wonderful way.*
- *I am a healthy person and I make healthy choices.*
- *I am a great cook and I love cooking.*
- *I don't eat processed foods.*
- *I enjoy eating healthy, good-quality foods.*

B) Write a list of the beliefs you have that empower you.

(You can come back and revisit these lists again and see how your feelings have shifted as you progress on your Artful Eating journey.)

You have the power to create massive changes in your life. Are you ready now to harness the vision of creating the life, body and health you desire? Then simply learn to choose the beliefs that empower you. Remember the Artful Eating philosophy is all about the mind! Once you choose to believe that you can achieve your goal, powerful shifts in mindset and behaviour will occur. It's time to create convictions that drive you in the direction of a body and life you desire. There is absolutely no reason to settle for anything less.

I now want you to build up the belief that you can and will achieve your goal easily and effortlessly.

Find a trigger that will make your decision to change become a conviction. Take the example of the choice to become a vegetarian. My father is in the meat industry and he used to buy me and my brother cows that would graze in the fields beside our home until it was time for them to go to the slaughterhouse. A dear friend, Lorna-Jane, became very fond of one of the cows we had, a beautiful white one we affectionately called Snowy. One day she came over and Snowy was gone. She asked where the beloved cow was, and my father in a deadpan way said, 'You're eating her!' He has a peculiar sense of humour, but Lorna-Jane did not find it funny. Quite the opposite, in fact: she was devastated. Around the same time, she watched the movie *Babe* (the one about the cute pig) and decided that she had a moral issue with eating these animals that she had so much affection

for. Her belief that it would be a good idea to become a vegetarian became a conviction. These were the trigger events that made her decision a conviction, and she is still a very happy and healthy vegetarian to this day!

Remember in Chapter 3, where I asked you to visualise your future? One where you maintained the current course you have been on, where you continue to struggle with your weight, and the other, where you decide to take action and experience the wonderful physical and mental changes. Return to that action now and do the visualisation once again, and listen to the visualisation audio (if you haven't already, you can access it at www.artful-eating.com). What is the trigger that you can hold on to that empowers a sense of conviction?

When it comes to this point in the Artful Eating journey, each of my clients has a different trigger, but the underlying motivation is ultimately the same:

To feel free.

Free from constantly thinking about food, free to eat what you want without constantly managing what you eat, free to wear the clothes you want, free from the health issues that are a consequence of being overweight, free to enjoy your body and to feel confident. Each action you take strengthens your emotions and therefore your conviction. Doing the actions throughout this book will help you believe and reinforce that conviction.

In order to feel the conviction that you can lose weight, develop a habit of focusing on the consequences of your beliefs. For example, focus on the fact that when you achieve your personal weight-loss goal, you will look and feel fantastic! We tend to believe that change takes a long time, but this is a myth. Think about the changes in your life: every significant change actually happened in a moment. It is what psychologists term the 'contemplation period' that actually takes time: this is the period of time when you are mentally preparing for change.

GET READY FOR CHANGE: *NOW*

The aim here is to change your beliefs and behaviours. Change how you feel about your body. I want you to understand that it's a complete myth that weight loss is an incredible struggle. Unfortunately losing weight is not thought of as a pleasurable experience, but it really can be!

The first belief we must have to create change is:

I can change, right now.

I know this is a big challenge. Already we have spoken about how typically there is the belief that significant change takes time. It's not change that takes time; it's mentally preparing to change. In reality, change takes an instant. I want you to make that instant right now. You can do it immediately!

The second important belief we must have to create change is:

You are responsible for your own change.

Only you. No one else. If you don't accept this, you will always be looking to someone else to make the change for you. So let's go through the 'how' of accomplishing change now. Some of this we have already covered, but it's such an important element of achieving your goal that we are going to revisit it.

Decide what your goal is.

Okay you have already done this, but what is holding you back from being this weight or size now?

Get specific: write it down.

Again, connecting with the idea of your own personal story, whatever you focus on in life is what you will experience. So if you focus on the idea that you are always late, then guess what? You will be late, as you will unconsciously create the conditions to support this belief. Likewise, if your story is 'I am fat and I don't like my body' and if you occupy your thoughts with negative beliefs about your body, you will take action to support this belief: by eating too much, bingeing or stuffing yourself with unhealthy foods and not enjoying your body.

It's time to change the focus. That's what this chapter is all about. Back in Chapter 1, I asked you to decide your goal. Revisit that now. I'm sure for many of you it felt a little bit unrealistic, or maybe you thought, 'This is my goal, but it's going to be really hard to achieve it.' Address that belief now. Decide how you want your life to be, how you want to feel in your body, how you want to experience your environment. The more specific you can be about it and the more clarity you have, the more momentum and conviction you will have to achieve this healthier, happier version of you more quickly. We have already explored what has prevented you from achieving that goal: your own disempowering personal story that you have carried around with you throughout your life.

Change is not a question of capability; it's a question of motivation, conviction and commitment. The problem for most people is that they struggle to link a sense of urgency to the change they want to achieve. In fact, I bet you can remember a time when you actually did lose weight, when you were completely committed to doing it, and I bet you were doing it in preparation for your wedding day or some big occasion, because there was an urgency attached to it. Generally, though, we put it off. We say, 'I'll start the diet tomorrow, or next Monday.' It feels like something we should do or ought to do someday, not something we absolutely must do right now. So you need to create a sense of urgency.

Now is the time.

Now is the time for you to enjoy the clothes you want to wear, have a body you love and feel confident about, to be healthy inside and out. So I'm going to ask you a few questions. Again,

we have touched on this in Chapter 1, but I want you to reinforce the wonderful work you have already done.

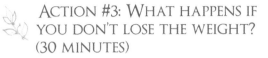

ACTION #3: WHAT HAPPENS IF YOU DON'T LOSE THE WEIGHT? (30 MINUTES)

Take the time to write out detailed answers to each of these questions:

WHERE WILL YOU BE FIVE YEARS FROM NOW IF YOU DO NOT LOSE THE WEIGHT?

WHAT WILL IT COST YOU IF YOU DON'T CHANGE?

WHAT WILL YOU MISS OUT ON IN YOUR LIFE IF YOU DON'T MAKE THIS SHIFT NOW?

What is it already costing you:

- *Mentally?*
- *Emotionally?*
- *Physically?*
- *Financially?*
- *Spiritually?*
- *Health wise?*
- *What is it inhibiting you from doing?*
- *How is it affecting your mental well-being?*

- *How is it affecting your quality of life?*

- *How is it affecting your relationships?*

Looking at your answers, take a few minutes to visualise your future self, embodying these conditions, staying the same, or indeed seeing your size, health and quality of life deteriorate. Really feel the feelings; visualise or think about it. Step into your future self's shoes, look at yourself in the mirror and see what you can see, feel what you can feel, and hear your thoughts and the thoughts and opinions of others, especially your loved ones. I want you to make the pain of not deciding to change so real, so tangible and intense that you simply cannot put off taking action any longer. Close your eyes, take a moment and really feel the sense of urgency and motivation for change right now.

ACTION #4: START TO LINK POSITIVE FEELINGS TO LOSING WEIGHT (30 MINUTES)

By linking positive feelings to the idea of changing and losing weight, you will really want it, believe you can achieve it and know that you are ready for it. Take the time to write out detailed answers to each of these questions. By taking action and committing to change now:

- *How will you feel about yourself?*

- *What kind of quality of life will*

you experience when you achieve your goal and have a body you love and appreciate?

- *How will your family and friends feel?*

- *How much happier will you be?*

- *How much healthier will you be?*

- *How much more energy will you have?*

- *How much more fun will it be to go clothes shopping and get dressed every morning?*

- *How confident will you feel?*

- *What thoughts will come to your mind when you look in the mirror?*

- *What thoughts will you have about yourself?*

- *How will loving your body and enjoying food affect the quality of your life?*

Again, assess your answers and take a few minutes to visualise your future self, embodying these conditions, this time committing to lasting change and reaping the rewards of that change in your health, appearance and confidence. Really feel the good feelings; visualise or think about them. Step into your future self's shoes, look at yourself in the mirror, and see what you can see, feel what you can feel, and hear your thoughts and the thoughts and opinions of others, especially your loved ones. Really take the time to feel how good it feels to enjoy life, food and your body, and to feel freedom from all the negative inner thoughts, hang-ups and restrictions you have felt for so long. The key here is to allow your imagination to flow and build up lots of wonderful, powerful reasons: reasons that are strong enough to change your actions and behaviours right now, not some time in the future.

After doing the above exercises, if you still don't feel completely ready, excited even, to take action and change now, then you don't have enough leverage. It's that simple. So revise the questions, revisit your new story and really work on generating a state of positive action. Focus on how wonderful it will feel when you achieve your goal and feel the freedom to eat what you want, to enjoy your food and to look amazing – because that is exactly what we are working towards! It may be that you need to do a bit more personal work on this, reading your new story every day, returning to these questions and visualising what it will feel like if you don't commit to change and if you do.

Do this mental practice daily: it will only take five minutes and I guarantee it will be the most effective and rewarding five minutes you spend! (You can even do it in the shower if you struggle to find some quiet time for yourself to do it.) Make the positive vision so real and tangible that you can feel the good, pleasurable feelings of being in that new body and new way of being.

This is the work, dear friend: not focusing on willpower, control, some diet plan, or cutting out the foods you love. This is the work: believing you can achieve your goal, deciding to take action and moving forward in this wonderful, powerful new way. The rest really is a piece of cake!

7

REALIGNMENT AND INTUITIVE EATING

'The more original a discovery, the more obvious it seems afterward.' Arthur Koestler

In this chapter you will:
gain clarity on what to eat and, more importantly, how to eat it
discover the biological imperative for privileging pleasure
learn the four steps to eating artfully
discover the three phases of healthy habit formation
discover the importance of feeling good in your body now.

It's finally time to explore what to eat and, more importantly, how to eat it! I am also going to share the essential healthy habits that will soon become part of the fabric of your Artful Eating way of life, where you will effortlessly and enjoyably lose weight and keep it off for life. Exciting, right?

The time when your body is realigning with how you want it to be should be an enjoyable period when you're not focusing on the scales.

Instead, you're working on your mindset and engaging with all the actions in this book. For some, realignment might not take very long, but for others it may take a bit more time. How quickly or slowly you lose weight varies from person to person. Generally, healthy weight loss consists of about 1–2 lb per week. If you have a lot of weight to lose, you might see bigger weight-loss results early on. But think of it as a gradual process, and trust that if you take the action you will achieve your goal. We are not robots, so generally we will not lose weight in a uniform way. You will find that you will drop a few pounds and then put one on, then go down a few more, then maintain that weight for a little while, and then drop a bit more!

At thirteen, I went to boarding school. In fact, I begged my parents to send me. Having read all the Mallory Towers and St Clare's books, I was consumed by Enid Blyton's idealised versions of the traditional girls' boarding school and so absolutely adored the idea of going away to school. I had this insatiably romantic idea of boarding school and just had to experience it for myself. Thankfully it did not disappoint. The school my parents sent me to was indeed quite magical. Many of the girls hailed from wonderfully exotic-sounding places like Tasmania, India, Hong Kong and the Cayman Islands (which to an Irish girl in 1994 sounded extremely impressive). It was, to me anyway, as if I had stepped into the pages of one of my beloved Blyton books. There was the stout, stern, bulldog-like 'Nurse', who had very little time for the silliness that comes with being a young teenage girl. This was perfectly counterbalanced by the kind-hearted, tall, slim and elegant Miss Clark, who had one glass eye, so you were never really sure who she was talking to. It felt like our principal, Miss Mew, came from another time. She dressed, head to toe and hair too, like a headmistress from the 1940s. I was in heaven! There were many, many, midnight feasts, we got up to all sorts of mischief and, most importantly, we had so much fun. Why I'm reminded of boarding school now and sharing my experience

here is because this was the place I first learned how to eat 'properly'. Now, please don't get me wrong: my mother instilled perfectly respectable table manners, but boarding school elevated a mealtime to an event that should be respected and enjoyed.

We were taught how to sit correctly: back straight and certainly no elbows on the table. Each meal consisted of a number of courses, none of which were too big. For the main meal of the day there was always a starter of usually either soup or a salad, followed by the main, and then dessert followed by fruit. We were encouraged to eat slowly, to chew our food, and to place the knife and fork down between mouthfuls. We were also taught the correct way to eat everything (even a burger and chips, a rare treat, were to be eaten with a knife and fork!). This education included how to peel an orange correctly, which genuinely fascinated me. You score the peel and pull off the skin a segment at a time, to reveal the juicy fruit underneath. It is very elegant and I felt quite the lady once I finally mastered it.

We were also encouraged to practise the art of good conversation, which was certainly elevated when we were at the headmistress's table. Mostly what I took from this education is that a mealtime is a time to stop work, relax and enjoy nourishing oneself. Mealtimes punctuated the long days and the multiple little courses meant that you had time for your body and mind to register that you were full, while never feeling stuffed. Because each mealtime was approximately an hour long, there was no rush and you had time to enjoy the company of others. We slowed down, savoured our food and chewed, and by eating 'correctly' I think it fostered a respect and appreciation for what we were served and how important nourishing ourselves was. It was this formative experience that sowed the seeds for my Artful Eating guide on 'how to eat' in the pages that follow.

Once you have completed the 48-hour Kick-starter Challenge, it is time to start realigning your body in order to achieve your goal weight. I am now going to teach you some really simple but absolutely vital steps in order to eat artfully and lose weight joyously. These steps are essential and must be incorporated into your daily eating habits.

Controversially, the British supermodel Kate Moss was famed for saying, 'Nothing tastes as good as skinny feels.' Kate was absolutely vilified for saying this, but it provides us with great psychological insight into how she associates pain with overeating and pleasure with being disciplined. I may be giving her the benefit of the doubt here, but this is a very helpful association. From now on you will train your brain to associate pleasure with the discipline of not finishing your portion and associate pain with overeating, stuffing your face and feeling really full and bloated. We have completely lost touch with our bodies, no longer listen to our gut, and eat far too much in general. There are four steps to eating artfully, and while they seem simple, they are at the centre of your ability to experience freedom with food while achieving your dream size.

HOW TO EAT

STEP 1: EAT THE BEST-QUALITY FOOD YOU CAN ACCESS

This is the baseline. Without it you are really going to struggle to enjoy your food. Unfortunately, we live in a time where food is mass-produced and force-grown, which really compromises the taste. We are so used to eating highly processed foods and eating automatically that we have lost touch with what food should taste like. Food should and can taste amazing, every time you eat it! I cannot impress upon you enough how important good ingredients are. The better the ingredients, the better the taste. The better the taste, the less you need to eat to feel satisfied. Also it means that you are fuelling your body with good things. In Chapter 11 I will talk about the financial cost of buying better food, but the basic principle is 'less is more'. Buy less, eat less, but eat well. When we favour quality over quantity, we are in line with Artful Eating. You will taste the difference, you will enjoy your food more, and weight loss will be a joyous consequence.

For far too long we have been influenced by weight-loss and diet regimes that propagate the idea that we should prohibit foods we love. First fat was bad, then sugar. Now 'clean eating' is the fad *du jour*. We are being overloaded with messages that tell us we should be eating mainly fruit and vegetables and juicing everything to lose weight. No wonder we are so lost. Every aisle of the supermarket is filled with all sorts of diet foods, diet versions of our favourite foods, and 'free from' foods. They have even now developed a 'low-fat cream': isn't that an oxymoron? The Artful Eating philosophy advocates balance in all things. It's not about being 'good' or avoiding whole food groups; instead, this is a holistic and practical approach to eating that is rooted in psychology.

I realised the importance of quality when it comes to food on our honeymoon. My husband Liam and I spent a glorious two weeks on the MS *Queen Elizabeth* liner, cruising around the Adriatic. I discovered, however, that we had unwittingly ended up in a pseudoscience experiment for the taste buds! The cruise attracted us for many reasons, my restlessness for one, and the thought that we could be on the move while we slept really appealed. Waking up in a different port, experiencing a different culture and different food, excited me, and I'm just not one for lying by the pool. The other draw was elegant fine dining with silver service every night! A huge fan of Evelyn Waugh's *Brideshead Revisited*, I loved the glamour and romance of his account of a cruise across the Atlantic, so in homage a cruise sounded magical, as we were required to don our best each night for the evening meal.

However, very quickly I noticed something inescapable: the food on-board, which was beautifully prepared and presented, couldn't hold a candle to the simple fare we were eating on the islands and inlets we stopped at each day. *The food simply tasted better.* It was fresh, less salty, bursting with flavour, simple, uncomplicated and so fabulously filling. While good-quality ingredients and fresh produce (the ultimate key to achieving weight loss) are things I have been an advocate of for a long time, the contrast in our daily fare was so striking that it left a lasting impression. I still remember the mouth-watering simple Greek salad we enjoyed in a tiny little restaurant in Crete: magnificent! So I encourage you to do your very best to eat good-quality, fresh ingredients. You will taste the difference, and as a result you will eat less, because tasty food is packed with flavour. As you savour the flavour, you will consciously chew and enjoy your food, eating more slowly and allowing your body and mind time to acknowledge that it has had enough.

I think this principle really counts when it comes to vegetables and fruit. Always, where you can, buy organic. I order from the local organic supermarket and they deliver to my door. I get a massive box of fruit and vegetables that are in season and so taste delicious! This box costs £18 (€20) and consists of the bulk of my food shop for the week. Buying organic doesn't have to cost the earth. Dairy, meat, pork, fish and poultry is another area where we should privilege quality. I only buy food sourced from reputable farms where the animals' welfare is prioritised. That means no over-milking, being grass-fed and essentially 'free range'. So farmed fish, for example, is out. I guarantee you will taste the difference. People often remark that my cakes taste delicious: that is because I'm using butter and milk made from grass-fed cows and eggs from free-range chickens. It is extremely inhumane how animals are treated within the food industry, and while I'm not vegan I am very cognisant of this fact and so very careful with what I eat and buy. While this is more expensive, we should aim to eat less, waste less and eat well.

Enjoying your food is the key to developing a healthier relationship with food. This goes for sweet things too. You are much better off spending £2.60 (€3) on a 100 g bar of delicious, organic fair-trade chocolate than you are buying a mass-produced and overly processed chocolate bar or a multi-pack for the same price. You will eat less and savour the delicious flavour. Win–win, right? So with this in mind I encourage you to know your food budget, make it count and favour quality over quantity.

Remember, if it tastes amazing you will need less of it to feel full as you savour each mouthful!

STEP 2: EAT INTUITIVELY

From now on, only eat when you are actually hungry. Do not eat just because someone offers you something, or because it's there, or because you are bored, sad, tired and so on. We will address how to overcome emotional eating in Chapter 9, but for now keep in mind that you only eat when your stomach sends you a message that you need some fuel. Food

is nutritious and enjoyable fuel. We should only eat when we need to, not when we see something we like or because it is a specific mealtime. Learn to tune in to your stomach; this is something I encouraged you to do on the 48-hour Kick-starter. Every time you go to eat something, ask yourself, 'Am I hungry right now? Do I need this or do I just fancy this?' Simply asking these questions before you eat will really help you lose weight and keep it off. Now, I do not want you to wait until you are starving!

Think of a hunger scale:

1. Physically faint
2. Ravenous
3. Hungry
4. Slightly hungry
5. Neutral
6. Pleasantly satisfied
7. Full
8. Stuffed
9. Nauseous

I want you to reside between hungry and satisfied. Never allow yourself to get to starving or to stuffed! You can achieve this by listening to your body. The more you tune into it, the more you will hear it. When you're in

the process of habit formation, check in with yourself on an hourly basis and feel where you are on the hunger scale. Once you notice that you're feeling slightly hungry, it's time to eat.

Step 3: Eat what you want and enjoy your food

What I am encouraging is a sense of the importance of pleasure around food. Sourcing it (from people who put love into their produce, which translates into taste), cooking it (with love, patience and with others), eating it (with a glass of something that will complement the meal), in a beautiful setting (effortlessly achieved with some flowers, nice tableware and candles), and being present in the moment.

I want to share with you some interesting research that I hope will help you to understand the magic of our innate biological imperative to enjoy our food. This is something I have long advocated from a psychological perspective, but now I understand the physiological necessity too.

In the 1930s, researchers conducted a fascinating study that would not be permitted today, in which a group of toddlers were put in charge of feeding themselves! This experiment beautifully demonstrates our innate nutritional wisdom. The children were offered thirty-four nutritionally diverse whole foods, including water, potatoes, beef, bone jelly, carrots, chicken, grains, bananas and milk. What each child ate, and how much, was entirely up to him or her.[1]

The results were astonishing. Instead of bingeing on the sweetest foods, the toddlers were drawn to the foods that best nourished them. They ate more protein during growth spurts, and more carbs and fat during periods of peak activity. After an outbreak of mononucleosis, curiously, they consumed more beef, carrots and beets. One child with a severe vitamin D deficiency even drank cod liver oil of his own volition until he was cured. By the end of the experiment, one doctor was so impressed with the toddlers' health that he described them as 'the finest group of specimens' he'd ever seen in their age group. So you see, we really need to start tuning into our body: it knows best! No more feeling guilty about food or what you have eaten. Food is a wonderful resource that you can and must enjoy. So eat what you actually want, not what you think you should eat. Listen to your body: it knows what you need to eat.

In another study, researchers fed two groups of women, one Swedish and one Thai, a spicy Thai meal. The Thai women, who presumably liked the meal more than the Swedish women did, absorbed almost 50 per cent more iron from it than their Swedish counterparts. A second condition followed: the meal was again served, but this time it was blended together into an almost unrecognisable mush. Interestingly, when the meal was served as a mushy paste, the Thai women absorbed 70 per cent less iron than they had before, from the exact same meal! The researchers concluded that food which is unfamiliar (Thai food to the Swedish women) or unappetising (mush rather than solid food) is less nutritious than food that looks, smells and tastes good to you. The explanation can be found in the digestive process itself, in the relationship between our gut and our brain.[2]

Imagine sitting in your favourite restaurant before a delicious plate of your favourite fare. The sights and smells evoke pleasure and tell your brain that the meal will be enjoyable. The brain responds by pushing your salivary glands into high gear and ordering your stomach to secrete more gastric juices, resulting in your body absorbing more nutrients, as your mind and body have prepared themselves for the food you're about to eat. This is in stark contrast to a pre-prepared diet dinner. This sight will result in your brain sending a less enthusiastic message to your mouth and stomach, causing the food to be less thoroughly digested and metabolised. So the nutritional value of food is a synergistic combination of the nutrients in the food and our reception of that food. If we remove enjoyment from the equation, the nutritional value of the food diminishes.

Another study, which it upsets me to share, as I hate animal testing, further supports this idea. Scientists destroyed the nerve centres of a group of rats so that they couldn't taste anything. The control group of rats, who luckily retained their nerve centres, and the rats without the ability to taste, were fed the exact same food. Alarmingly, over a short period of time, the rats who had lost their ability to taste died, while their counterparts who could still taste were thriving.[3]

During autopsy, the researchers found that even though the rats had eaten the same healthy amount of food as the control group, they had died of malnutrition. Their organs had wasted away as if they had been starved, indicating that because they could not taste the food, they could not absorb the nutrients they needed to sustain themselves.

Add to this the fact that when you eat fat or protein your body produces the chemical cholecystokinin (CCK). CCK aids digestion by stimulating the small intestines, pancreas, gallbladder and stomach. Once CCK is released, it then shuts down appetite by sending a message to the hypothalamus to say you've had enough. Finally, it stimulates the sensation of pleasure in the cerebral cortex to tell you to enjoy. All this is triggered as soon as we eat fat or protein. This magical little chemical functions to metabolise our meal, tells us when to finish our meal, and tells us to enjoy it while we eat it. Isn't the body truly marvellous?[4]

So to feel satiated we must recognise that pleasure, metabolism and appetite all function in a synergistic way if we allow them to. Unfortunately, we are used to thinking of pleasure as completely separate to the nutritional process. Worse still, we are now conditioned to think that if we're enjoying our food it's probably not good for us, as we worry that we won't be able to stop eating it. My clients often tell me that they will actually avoid the food they enjoy altogether for fear of bingeing. Yet the effects of CCK indicate the exact opposite is true.

Interestingly, one of the chemicals that increases our appetite is neuropeptide Y, which tells us to search for food. This chemical is naturally elevated in the morning, as we are in need of fuel for the day. It's also raised when we are deprived of food, especially when we are dieting, by sending the message to encourage us to eat carbohydrates. If you eat mainly low-calorie food or if you restrict yourself to a bland diet, your body will respond by chemically demanding pleasurable foods to feel satiated. So we really need to recognise that neuropeptide Y indicates that we cannot escape the biological imperative to experience pleasure and enjoy our food.[5]

Further compelling evidence that we must enjoy comes from how endorphins function. Endorphins, typically associated with pleasure, are reproduced naturally throughout the body, most notably in the brain and the digestive system. One of their most significant functions is to make us feel happy. Just by eating, our endorphins are elevated, which supports the idea that eating is an inherently pleasurable experience. Another function of endorphins is that they stimulate fat mobilisation, so the same chemical that makes you happy also makes you burn fat! Add to this the fact that the greater the endorphin release in your digestive tract, the more blood and oxygen will be delivered there. This translates into increased digestion, assimilation and essentially greater efficiency in burning calories.[6]

From both a biological and psychological position, eating the best-quality food available and enjoying it is essential. This makes perfect sense, as our body is hardwired to find pleasure in eating good food and this in turn fuels our metabolism. It really is a beautiful system, which we should appreciate and respect. Stop trying to override your body's natural urges to enjoy. Listen to your body, eat foods you enjoy and feel the pleasurable feelings, trusting that these are triggering your metabolism and also triggering feelings of fullness. We have a beautifully balanced system within us: it's time to allow it to thrive!

When you are hungry, sit down at the table. Set your place. Always use a knife and fork. Mentally prepare yourself to eat and recognise that it is a pleasurable process. Smell the food, chew each mouthful and contemplate the taste. You should hear me at mealtimes, I make such a racket with my mmm's because I am really taking the time to taste my meal! When you're eating, it is important to be present in the moment and focus on the food you are eating. Take the time to smell it, anticipate it and savour it. Importantly, chew each mouthful. Initially, try chewing it twenty times. Always put the knife and fork, sandwich, fruit or treat down between mouthfuls and allow yourself time to chew. We are so used to gobbling down our food that we don't give our bodies time to recognise we are full, so it is essential to eat slowly and artfully, enjoying, savouring and chewing every single bite. In doing this, your stomach will have time to send a message to the brain that it is full. This usually takes twenty minutes. Remember, every meal or snack is an opportunity to feel happy and pleasurable.

STEP 4: WHEN YOU FEEL SATISFIED, STOP EATING

When practising this step, remember the hunger scale. There is no need to eat everything on your plate, especially when eating shop-bought portions or eating out. We tend to ingest far more food than we need to, based on commercial portion sizes. Deli baguettes are probably twice the size of what you need, but because they are larger, the shop can charge more for them. Disturbingly, we are now being conditioned to eat larger and larger sizes, and this is spilling over into our homes. Looking to this chart, which compares serving sizes in the 1980s with those today, we can see the alarming growth in portion sizes.

SERVING SIZES: THEN AND NOW

Food or beverage	1980s (calories)	Today (calories)
Turkey sandwich	320	820
French fries	210	610
Bagel	140	350
Slice of pizza	500	850
Soda	85	250

(*National Heart, Lung and Blood Institute; US Department of Health and Human Services*)

Use your hand as a guide:

- *A portion of pasta, rice or potatoes should be about the size of the front of your clenched fist- which is the equivalent of about half a cup.*

- *A serving of meat, fish or chicken should be about the size of your palm.*

- *Your fingertip is the size of about a teaspoon of butter.*

- *Your thumb, from your knuckle to the tip, is about the size of a tablespoon (a good measure for sauces, jams or condiments).*

- *A clenched fist is roughly the size of one cup (or a double serving of ice cream).*

I also encourage you to shrink the size of your plate. During the process of realignment, use a side plate, and a small cup, glass and bowl. An average plate is about 25 cm in diameter, but if you shift to a 20 cm plate, you will reduce the amount you eat by about 20 per cent. This is a really easy shift that will significantly decrease your food intake. Furthermore, research shows that if you dish up your food and leave the pot on the stove you are less likely to go back for seconds; in fact, on average you will eat about 18 per cent less![7] Remember you can always go back for more if you are still hungry, but rethinking your portion size is essential.

From now on, stop eating when you feel satisfied. While you are in the process of realignment, start by having a half portion of absolutely everything: half an apple(!), half a slice of quiche, half a sandwich and so on. As you do this, you are changing your habits around food and retraining your brain to eat what you need to, not what a portion size or the diameter of your plate decides! Halve absolutely everything, eat as long as you feel hungry, remembering you can always go back for more, should you still feel hungry, and stop when you begin to feel full.

I advocate eating what you want, but it must be accompanied by listening to your body. When you have had enough, stop eating! This is a muscle that you need to exercise to develop, as we have long lost the art of eating until we are full and instead eat until there is nothing left.

HEALTHY-EATING HABIT FORMATION

Initially you will find taking up these new habits will require constant conscious practise. But once you work through the habit formation cycle, these behaviours will become second nature. I was just speaking with a client of mine today, Marianne, who began her Artful Eating journey five months ago. As I write this, it is a cold and crisp January morning and everywhere the 'new year, new you' diet message is taking hold. She was so excited and had to share with me that this year over the Christmas period she didn't gain an ounce! Normally she would have gained about seven pounds over the holidays, but without any conscious effort and without any restricting or denying herself, she managed to sail through the party season eating and

enjoying her food. This is because she had already done the groundwork and assimilated the Artful Eating philosophy and these four steps into her life. Another client of mine, who is a school principal, described Artful Eating as an education. I love this description, as it aptly describes the process: once you learn something, it cannot be unlearned!

So I'm now going to teach you what I call the habit-formation cycle. Read this closely and perhaps return to it a couple of times over the next few weeks, as you work your way through the different stages of habit formation. If you follow these instructions closely you will find yourself effortlessly and easily maintaining this way of eating for life. What this means is that, just like Marianne, you'll find that you can enjoy food, eat what you like and not gain any weight. Indeed, during the realignment period, when you are consciously working towards your goal weight, you'll find that you actually lose weight by sticking to the four steps described above.

Through working with my clients, I have observed that the establishment of a habit can be understood in three stages.

Stage one is the 'positive adoption stage', where you find that your enthusiasm makes the new habit seem easy. We can recognise this easily in January when the gyms are bursting with people full of motivation as they easily stick to their new year's resolutions. Or you might have experienced this in the first flush of a new diet, when you feel extremely committed, buy all the

ingredients, apparatus and gear, and easily stick to the rigid regime. So the 'positive-adoption stage' usually occurs due to something inspiring (like reading this book!) and you will find that maintaining the new habit is easy as you feel determined to create change.

The second stage sees the initial enthusiasm wane as the reality of the effort and commitment involved begins to become apparent. This is when it's very important to recognise and associate pleasure with the new habit and its outcomes, and pain with the old way of behaving. The 'perseverance stage' requires just that: perseverance! At this point you may find the old habits creeping back in, like eating when you are not actually hungry, or not stopping when you recognise you are full. This is the most challenging stage of habit formation and there are a few things that you can do to help push through and persevere. As with so many aspects of Artful Eating, the best thing you can do when you hit this initial wall is to become aware of it and to acknowledge it. By consciously recognising that you are coming up against resistance, you can then do something about it. By persevering and forcing yourself to enact the healthy habit a couple of times, you will see that you can easily push through this stage and work towards consolidating the habit.

Each time that you experience the struggle to enact the habit, acknowledge it, bring your awareness to it, think about and feel the good feelings that persevering will bring – freedom around food, achieving your goal, actually enjoying food – and harness this power to enact the healthy habit. Conversely, if you choose not to persevere when confronted with resistance, it will become easier to give in the next time you come up against resistance.

By bringing your awareness to the resistance, you are in a position to consciously acknowledge both the pros of persevering and the cons of giving in to your old unhelpful ways. So when you encounter resistance, ask yourself: how will you feel if you give in or if you persevere? Remember to feel the pleasure of achieving your goal at this moment and, conversely, to feel the pain of giving in and not making the change you desire. Use the power of projection, something we have looked at in the visualisation exercise in Chapters 3 and 6. Look to your future. Imagine your life in great detail five years from now, having not made the changes. How will you look and feel? What will the quality of your health and relationships be like? Really go into detail here and allow yourself to feel the consequences of not taking action and sticking to your healthy habits. This is a very powerful and effective tool to help you persevere and feel motivated to keep practising the healthy habit!

Once you have overcome the first two stages, you will reach what I like to call 'unconscious integration'. This stage is characterised by Marianne, who over the Christmas period found herself effortlessly practising the Artful Eating philosophy without any conscious effort. It just came naturally to her. However, there are a couple of things to be wary of once you reach this stage. One is negative thoughts, to which we are especially susceptible if we feel that we are not experiencing results quickly enough: thoughts such as, 'This isn't working for me' or 'I can't do it, I always fail.' When you feel these thoughts encroaching, acknowledge them and answer back with a positive affirmation that resonates with you, like, 'I can and I will succeed, because I'm ready and I want to.' Hold on to that determination and feel the empowering feelings connected with it. Emotions are extremely powerful, so utilise them and leverage them in a positive way. Remember that what you think will determine your actions. So again, practise awareness and take action!

When we are in the flow and at the unconscious integration stage, we are still susceptible to significant disruptions, such as illness, stressful life events or even just a holiday or your routine being interrupted. Again awareness is key here. If you find that you've fallen back to the perseverance stage, acknowledge it and use the strategies I suggested to get back on track. Remember that each time you persevere, you are reinforcing and strengthening your commitment and conviction. Like a muscle, the new healthy habit is becoming stronger and you are that bit closer to these healthy habits becoming the only way you eat.

Assimilating this new approach to eating will take time and effort, but it will be enjoyable as you discover how to really taste and savour your food. Shifting to this new way of being where you now automatically eat without overindulging to the point of feeling stuffed, and listen to your body, only eating the food you actually want, is incredibly rewarding. These are such positive and liberating habits that it should not require too much effort on your part to reach the unconscious integration stage. How long that actually takes depends on each individual, but have faith. Focus on the pleasure of adopting these healthy behaviours and you will have mastered the key to eating what you want and enjoying food freedom, all the while working towards your goal. Now, doesn't that sound worthwhile? Remember that a habit is formed and reinforced on a daily basis, so take it one day at a time. Also, each time you find yourself back at the perseverance stage, trust that once you push through you will reach a new level of assimilation, reinforcing the unconscious integration stage.

STOP TRYING TO LOSE WEIGHT AND FEEL GOOD IN YOUR BODY NOW

There is just one more healthy habit I encourage you to foster, and it might actually be more challenging than the practical steps laid out above.

Stop trying to lose weight and feel good in your body now.

I love this sentiment and it's incredibly important. Thinking back on my time in London when I was unhappy with my body, I felt so uncomfortable in my skin. I hated choosing what to wear in the morning and I absolutely dreaded getting dressed up to go out. When I looked in the mirror, all I could see were my flaws. I obsessed over the scales and a pound up or down determined how my day would go. It is ridiculous when I think about it now, as our body weight naturally fluctuates up and down a couple of pounds. I was so caught up with trying to lose weight that I just could not enjoy or appreciate my body.

All this brought was misery. By constantly focusing on what was wrong, I just reinforced negative behaviours, which then in turn reinforced the negative beliefs. By thinking that losing weight was difficult and by feeling unhappy with my body, I found that this was my reality. My eating patterns supported these thoughts as I oscillated from diet food to bingeing on rubbish, and by not feeling good in my body I failed to treat it with the love and respect it deserved. I now understand that when we feel good the opposite occurs: we do positive things, we eat well, we are more active, and we look and feel better in ourselves.

With this in mind, I encourage you to fall in love with your body. Cast your mind back. Can you remember a time when you loved your body? If so, visualise that size and visualise how that felt. Take a moment each day to do this. If you don't remember a time, then pick someone who has a body you admire and visualise it as being yours. Feel the good feelings that come from having this body that you love. Use the cognitive hypnosis audio that accompanies this book (at https://www.artful-eating.com/) and listen to it daily, as it will help reinforce what I am asking you to do.

Be kind to your body. Start to respect it and think about all the things you love about it. One of the biggest barriers to weight loss is the psychological barrier. If you think thin, you will become thin. Stop looking enviously at slim people. Start reframing in your mind how you view your body. 'Thinking thin' will give you the psychological empowerment (not willpower) to make healthy choices in line with this new phase in your life where you eat artfully and enjoy feeling healthy and beautiful inside and out.

Practise these steps, as it will take time to adjust and reach the stage of unconscious integration. Remember, the eyes are bigger than the stomach! Revisit this chapter a couple of times until you become familiar with the steps outlined. Knowing which stage of habit formation you are in will be helpful when you come up against the inevitable blocks and resistances. Be kind to yourself as you begin to let go of the old unhealthy and unhelpful habits you probably practised for a lifetime. Acknowledge your successes and take it one day at a time. What I'm teaching you here is how to eat intuitively. You will find that you really enjoy this shift in how you eat.

WELL-BEING AND DAILY RITUALS

'You will never change your life until you change something you do daily. The secret of your success is found in your daily routine.' John C. Maxwell

In this chapter you will:
find a mindful morning routine that will ensure you start the day on the right foot
learn the easiest and most beneficial ways to incorporate exercise into your daily routine
discover why you must privilege water over all other beverages (even champagne!)
learn why sleep is vital for mental well-being, physical vitality and as a weight-loss aid.

In this chapter we are going to get practical. I want to enthuse you with a sense of the importance of both physical and psychological well-being, as these two aspects are central to the Artful Eating philosophy. The daily rituals I advocate will help you practise self-love and self-respect and set you up for success. I think perhaps the most important lesson I've learned in my life so far – and it's one my clients have taught me – is to love yourself. Love and treat yourself like you love and treat those special people in your life: your children, family, friends and pets. Self-love is not a narcissistic pursuit; it is a necessary baseline for feeling good, enjoying life and enjoying others. Looking good is a happy consequence.

It may take a bit of effort to begin with, but allowing yourself to look in the mirror and focus on the good bits, not the flaws, is a lovely start. Instead of homing in on the thing you did wrong, focus for a couple of seconds on the thing you did right. When we love and respect ourselves we are much more inclined to do things that serve us, like eating well, minding our physical health and believing we can achieve our goals.

Research within the field of Positive Psychology has a lot to contribute to this idea of being in a position of self-love, which actually facilitates feeling happy and achieving your goals. If you ask someone why they are unhappy, they will usually tell you about something which is going on in their external world, or they'll say it's because of their genes: they have a family history of mental illness, or obesity, or a neurochemical imbalance. The current understanding is that we are a result of our genes and our environment.

When researching happiness, however, positive psychologists found that long-term happiness is actually very difficult to predict when looking at one's external circumstances. Taking into account all the major external factors, for example how much money you make, where you live, what your education level is, whether you're married or not, how many children you have and so on, it is possible to predict short-term happiness with a great degree of accuracy. For example, if you eat a chocolate bar, you will feel happier, but five minutes later you may think, 'Why did I do that?'

But when looking at long-term levels of happiness, or your joy and well-being over a longer period of time, psychologists can only predict 10 per cent of the variability of happiness amongst people. In the long term, happiness is not about your external circumstances; it's about how your brain processes the world you find yourself in.[1]

How you process the life you have, the size you are and, most importantly, your relationship with yourself, is to do with the position you take up in the world, not your circumstances. If you change the lens through which you view the world and your experience of it, you will actually dramatically increase your level of happiness, well-being and self-love.

Unfortunately, most people follow a formula for happiness and success that's actually backwards, which limits happiness and inhibits your ability to achieve your goals. Think about how often you say to yourself, 'As soon as I lose the weight I'll feel good about myself' or 'as soon as I fit into that outfit I'll like myself' or 'as soon as I meet the right partner I'll feel happier'.

The problem is, every time you achieve your goal your brain changes the goalposts of what you desire. So if you achieve your desired weight, you suddenly feel you need to lose more. Or you unconsciously sabotage yourself by regaining the weight, as you cannot handle achieving your goal. This is because you think you should feel happy once you have achieved your desire, but in actual fact the satisfaction eludes you.

So we need to turn the formula on its head. What psychologists have found is that when the brain is in a position of feeling positive, our ability to achieve our goal or desired outcome improves dramatically.

A lot of people think that happiness can be reduced to genes and one's environment, but research proves that it's absolutely not true. Positive psychologists conducted an experiment where the participants were required to record three things they were thankful for every evening for a week. By the end of the experiment they had twenty-one things that they were thankful for, which is wonderful, but not actually the point. Happiness is a pattern within the brain and you can actually learn to be in a state of happiness – not if you introduce isolated bursts of changes to your life, but by creating positive daily rituals.[2]

As the participants started their day thinking of three things they were grateful for, they began to retrain their brain. Instead of scanning the world for what they felt they were lacking, or automatically attuning to what was wrong in their lives, they began to attune to the things that provided meaning and joy. They had shifted their thinking towards a 'happiness advantage', with remarkably positive effects. Their health and well-being improved, their relationships improved, and their ability to achieve their goals improved.

This experiment shows that we can literally train our brains to become more optimistic. Wonderfully, this works with young children and grumpy old men! This is so powerful because people really believe that they can't move beyond their situation, but you absolutely can! With this in mind, I want you to start by consciously shifting to a position of gratitude and happiness in order to allow for some self-love. It's time to create some new thought patterns and daily rituals.

Before we delve into the daily rituals I advocate, I have a very powerful intention that a truly inspiring client shared with me. A young boy of nine came to my practice because he was embarrassed about his nail-biting habit. He had tried all the typical things one does to kick it: that awful-tasting nail varnish, wearing gloves, asking his family to remind him when he was doing it, but nothing had worked. So he asked his parents if he could get some outside help, and that's where I came in. Over the course of our work together, this wonderful boy came to his own simple yet profound realisation. As he was a very creative and thoughtful person, I asked him to design a family crest. He took his time and drew a beautiful crest, and I asked him to include a family motto. I was completely blown away by what he came up with. Crowning his lovely drawing was the motto: 'Make it a want, not a have to.'

I think this is a fabulous sentiment and one that empowered him to easily stop biting his nails. As soon as he shifted from feeling like this was something he had to do to something he actually wanted to do, he found the conviction and strength to effortlessly achieve it. I love this sentiment and I have to say I use it myself and share it with all my clients – and now, dear reader, with you! So before you embark on these new daily rituals, think about the positive outcomes and make incorporating them into your life a want, not a have to.

ACTION #1: MORNING RITUALS (20 MINUTES A DAY)

How we start our day is extremely important. Researchers have found that self-control and energy are not only intricately linked but also finite, daily resources that tire much like a muscle. The trick is to do the right things in the morning that will make your energy and self-control last as long as possible so that you will make healthy food choices throughout the day. I want you to incorporate this wonderful morning routine so that it automatically becomes part of the fabric of your day. Starting the day in the right way will set you up for a positive one where you are motivated and enjoy the Artful Eating philosophy. If you have little ones, do these practices with them, as they will gain the wonderful benefits too!

1. TEN THANKFUL THINGS EXERCISE

Each morning, before you get out of bed, count ten things that you feel thankful for, one on each finger. The key here is to really feel the good feelings of gratitude as you do this. At least five should pertain to you: what you're thankful for about yourself, both physical and mental. Just by committing to this simple, truly lovely exercise, you will begin to notice a shift in your thoughts as you start to move from feeling negative about yourself and your body to being

kinder and more respectful. Good things will come from this, I promise you. The aim here is for you to train your brain to feel positive and to become attuned to the good things in your life (believe me, there are many!). Even my most sceptical clients and those who come to me feeling genuine despair manage, with a little effort, to do this exercise. Over time they come to love and rely on it to foster a sense of well-being and happiness.

2. PRACTISE DAILY MEDITATION

Pretty much every great thought leader out there waxes lyrical on the transformative powers of meditation. For those of you who are sceptical about the truly magical powers of sitting with your breathing for a couple of minutes a day, I'm going to go into a little more detail on the benefits of meditation to really get you committed to and enthusiastic about it!

Meditation reduces both depression and anxiety

It makes sense that if you're feeling anxious an activity focused on clearing your mind of stress and slowing down will have a positive effect. This is exactly what a meta-analysis of dozens of studies into the benefits of meditation found. A daily meditation practice improves anxiety and depression levels within eight weeks on average.[3]

It improves your concentration and makes you smarter

Another study of meditation found that as few as four (yes, four!) twenty-minute meditation sessions can have a positive impact on your working memory, visuospatial processing and verbal fluency.[4]

Meditation actually makes you healthier

Meditation improves the immune system and helps fight off illnesses and reduces stress-induced immune problems.[5]

Meditation makes you more productive

If you struggle to focus when you are overwhelmed and find yourself switching between tasks without making any progress, then meditation helps with this too. Regular meditators tend to switch tasks less often and have better focus, as well has having better memory for tasks they have completed.[6]

Meditation makes you realise what's important

There is a wisdom that one develops and nurtures through meditation. Researchers have found that meditators have 'significantly larger' volumes in their orbito-frontal cortex (the home of grey matter) and the right hippocampus. These areas of the brain are associated with emotional regulation and response control, meaning that the more developed they are the better equipped we find ourselves to handle the vicissitudes of life.[7]

Finally (and my personal favourite), meditation helps you to love your body

One study shows that as little as three weeks of meditation can significantly reduce body dissatisfaction by focusing on self-compassion.

The reduction in body shame had a huge impact on the participants' self-worth and body appreciation, and, most impressively, this change lasted well after the meditation programme finished. So meditate and realise you can love and appreciate your body now for the beautiful thing that it is.[8]

These are just some of the benefits of meditation. I hope they have enlightened and motivated you to make meditation a wonderful addition to your daily rituals. You can download a meditation app, listen to some tranquil music and focus on your breathing, or choose a mantra and repeat it: really, whatever works for you.

3. INTEND YOUR DAY

This morning ritual will only take two minutes and we have already discussed the power of visualisation in Chapter 3. By mapping out your day in detail and seeing it going well, your intention will inform your actions, expectations and behaviour. Do this after you have completed your meditation.

Visualise:

- *eating healthy food and feeling fantastic about it*

- *not finishing everything on your plate and feeling the pleasure of not finishing*

- *having a happy, productive enjoyable day (go into a bit of detail here: what do you need to accomplish today?)*

- *feeling good in your body and enjoying what you're wearing*

- *feeling confident with each interaction you make with the people you meet and work with throughout the day*

- *smiling and making the people around you smile*

- *feeling in control of your thoughts and emotions*

- *enjoying your day full of confidence and happiness*

Go into as much detail as possible. The key is to really see it: see the bus arriving on time, see your boss smiling and saying 'good job' and so on. This also helps set a course for the day when you feel calm, collected and happy. This morning ritual will set you up for the day and will help you make the right choices that support your desire to lose weight and feel fantastic.

EXERCISE

Do you remember what I said about self-control? We only have a finite amount of it. When you exert self-control, you become mentally fatigued. When we experience this ego depletion, we are less able to use self-control again. So think about when you force yourself to go to the gym: if it's not something you enjoy, you're going to be tired from the physical activity, but you're also going to be mentally exhausted because you're doing something that you dislike. Unless you actually enjoy working out, which I know many people do, forget about it. Physical activity is essential for your mental well-being and your physical well-being, but the key is to find a physical activity that you enjoy for its own sake as opposed to for the purpose of weight loss. Think of it as finding a new hobby that you incorporate into your life and which also happens to be beneficial to your physical vitality and mental well-being.

Whether or not you have a sport you enjoy, you must begin walking. There are so many physical and psychological benefits of walking, and it is really the easiest activity that you can incorporate into your daily routine. Here are some of the benefits of walking to get you motivated.

IT MAKES YOU FEEL BETTER

Walking at a fast pace for ten minutes a day improves your mood for up to two hours! Researchers found that when people walked at a pace similar to that which they might use when running a few minutes late, they felt that the things that had been bothering them earlier seemed less problematic.[9]

IT HELPS KEEP YOUR ENERGY LEVELS UP

When you've finished your meal, instead of feeling energised often you feel sluggish as your body is digesting. This is the optimal time to go for a brisk fifteen-minute walk, as it significantly improves your body's ability to regulate its blood-sugar levels and avoid the mid-afternoon slump. Timing is everything with this: a short fifteen-minute walk after a meal is more beneficial for our energy levels than a longer walk at another time.[10]

IT STAVES OFF HEART DISEASE AND HELPS YOU LIVE LONGER

A brisk walk that elevates the heart rate can have great benefits, but if a brisk walk feels too challenging, then you can increase the length of your walk and still experience great benefits.[11]

IT KEEPS YOUR BRAIN YOUNG

As we get older, our hippocampus can shrink by up to 1 per cent a year. A shrinking brain is not good, as this can lead to problems with memory loss and even dementia. However, a 2011 study showed that walking for forty minutes three times a week can not only stave off the decline in brain size, but lead to an increase in size![12]

IT KEEPS THE WEIGHT OFF

A fifteen-year-long study looked at the relationship between walking and weight gain and found that those who walked thirty minutes a day were on average 17 lb lighter than those who did not.[13]

ACTION #2: TAKE THE 10,000-STEPS-A-DAY CHALLENGE (1 HOUR)

Get yourself a pedometer or download one on your phone and get stepping. Ten thousand steps is between four and five miles distance (or eight kilometres). If you walk reasonably fast, it should take about an hour; a slower pace will take two. An added benefit to a ten-thousand-step goal is that you will burn approximately 100 calories per mile: that's between 400 and 500 calories a day!

Initially this may seem like a challenge, but once you get used to it you will realise it's rather easy to achieve. You're going to love getting active: it clears the mind and feels wonderful. This should be an enjoyable challenge, so have fun with it and remember to make it a 'want', not a 'have to'! Here are some tips to help you:

- *Start early by getting a few thousand steps in before midday, this will help you feel motivated and it's a great way to start your day. You could do this by walking to work or walking your children to school. If the distance is too far, you could just walk part of the way.*

- *Whenever you're chatting on the phone, get up and walk around.*

- *Throughout the day, take a walking break. Every two hours or so, get up and do 1,000 steps.*

- *Get in the habit of taking the long way round to go anywhere or get anything.*

- *Park your car at the furthest point from the entrance in the car park,*

and get off the bus or train a stop early.

❧ *Walk 5,000 steps away from your home and then you'll have to walk the 5,000 steps back!*

❧ *Walk your dog. This is my absolute favourite activity and I do it every day.*

❧ *Go walking with a friend. I will always choose to walk with a friend rather than catch up over a cup of coffee.*

❧ *Always take the stairs. Wherever you are, have the attitude that 'I don't take the lift or escalators'. Once this is firmly in your mind, it's simply not an option.*

❧ *Track your goal using a pedometer: this will help you keep motivated and committed to reaching your daily steps goal.*

ACTION #3:
DRINK MORE WATER

Another essential healthy habit you must incorporate into your daily routine is to drink more water. Researchers have found that drinking water increases the rate at which people burn calories. The impact is modest, but after drinking approximately 17 oz of water, the subjects' metabolic rates increased by 30 per cent. Over the course of a year, drinking an extra 1.5 litres a day could burn 17,400 calories, a weight loss of approximately 5 lb. Up to 40 per cent of the increase in calorie burning is caused by the body's attempt to heat the water, so keep your water chilled.[14]

While this is a very small effect, just a few calories a day, often we think we are hungry when we are actually dehydrated. So sipping water will also help stave off hunger. Every time you find yourself feeling a little peckish or a little bit hungry, have a glass of chilled water. Make water your number one beverage of choice. If you aren't a big fan of water, turn to the 48-hour Kick-starter, where you will find simple yet glorious ways to flavour water.

I highly recommend that you get a water purifier, as tap water can be full of chemicals and unnecessary additives that aren't very pure at all. If you are prepared to invest, point-of-use water filters remove lead from drinking water, while countertop filters provide clean, healthy water that costs much less than bottled water, and they are more environmentally friendly too. It is thought that water filters greatly reduce the risk of rectal cancer, colon cancer and bladder cancer by removing chlorine and chlorine by-products from drinking water.[15] Convincing enough for you? Go grab a glass of chilled, filtered water and enjoy it.

ACTION #4:
BECOME A SLEEPING BEAUTY

I have always been a huge advocate of sleep and

adore hitting the pillow. The optimal amount of sleep obviously varies from person to person, but you should aim for about eight to eight and a half hours a night. There is some compelling research that should encourage you to take your sleep seriously, if you don't already do so.

MISSING OUT ON SLEEP CAN LEAD TO WEIGHT GAIN

Researchers found that people who sleep less than seven hours per night are heavier, gain more weight over time and have a harder time losing weight. In a study of middle-aged women, researchers concluded that there is a direct correlation between the amount of sleep the subjects received and weight gain. This study began over twenty years ago and includes more than 68,000 women who were asked in two-year intervals about their sleep patterns and their weight. The findings have revealed that those women who slept fewer than five hours a night weigh on average 5.4 lb more than the women who slept seven hours a night. In addition, those who slept fewer than five hours per night were actually 15 per cent more likely to become obese.[16]

IT STOPS LATE-NIGHT SNACKING

Sleep-deprived people can take in up to 500 extra calories compared with those who manage to get seven to eight hours sleep a night. The extra calories tended to come from more fatty and sugary foods.[17]

IT MAKES YOU LESS HUNGRY

Sleep deprivation sends our bodies into preservation mode, with our metabolism slowing to conserve energy. This corresponds with our bodies releasing the hormone ghrelin, which increases our appetite and encourages us to seek more food. By getting a good night's sleep we can maintain our natural balance and keep our hunger signals honest.[18]

IT HELPS YOU LOSE FAT

When we talk about losing weight, the desire is really to lose excess fat. But no matter how hard we try, if we aren't getting enough sleep it just won't work. Those who don't get enough sleep will lose 55 per cent less fat than those who make similar efforts and do sleep.[19]

IT HELPS YOU CONTROL YOUR PORTION SIZES

When we are sleep deprived we are more likely to give ourselves bigger portions, regardless of how hungry we are, as it's harder for us to hear the signals our body is sending to tell us we're full. The signals that do get through have been affected by the hormonal changes that our body goes through when we don't get enough sleep.[20]

With these wonderful benefits in mind, create your own bedtime routine. This will help to regulate your body and prepare your mind for sleep.

- Switch off your phone and computer.

- Make sure your bed is always welcoming: change your sheets regularly, so they smell lovely and inviting.

- Place a couple of drops of lavender oil on your pillow as it promotes sleep and smells delicious.

- Have a few sets of comfortable pyjamas or nightdresses that you enjoy wearing.

- Try having a cup of camomile tea before bed. Drinking herbal tea is a part of my bedtime ritual; it helps me unwind and relax after a long day.

- Blackout curtains or a really good eye mask are essential for a good night's sleep.

- If you struggle to wake with your alarm in the morning, this implies that you haven't had enough sleep. You should wake feeling refreshed and well rested, so try going to bed earlier or rearranging your schedule so that you can spend more time in bed in the morning.

- If you wake during the night, try counting backwards from three hundred in threes: this is more effective than counting sheep.

- If you find it hard to fall asleep, trying reading a chapter of a good book before bed, or listen to an audiobook and put it on a sleep timer so it will turn off once you have dozed off.

- If you find that you are wide awake, then do not lie in bed. Get up and make yourself a cup of herbal tea or go to the living room and read a book until you feel tired again, then go back to bed. Try not to lie in bed tossing and turning, as this will create negative associations. You want to think of your bed as the place that you enjoy sleeping.

If you think you might suffer from insomnia, see a doctor as soon as possible. There may be a medical reason for being unable to get to sleep, or it might be psychological, in which case working with a good therapist can help to remedy this. Prolonged interrupted sleep wreaks havoc on your system, so do not let sleep issues persist! If you have little ones, like I do, this can be particularly difficult, as new parents inevitably experience a lack of sleep and prolonged periods of interrupted sleep. If this is the case for you, do ask for help from loved ones and make the effort to sleep when your baby does during the day. I also encourage you to get your baby into a good sleep routine; there are lots of helpful resources available to advise you on this. Remember, your baby needs a good night's sleep as much as you do!

What we do consistently shapes us inside and out. This chapter has looked at extremely simple, indeed fundamental, daily rituals that you can easily incorporate into your routine. Have fun with these rituals and make them work for you. As I have said before, this is a holistic approach to a healthier and happier lifestyle, so taking care of yourself and investing in yourself is absolutely key. Also, as you incorporate these habits you can share them with your family and enjoy watching them benefit from a more intentional way of living.

OVERCOME EMOTIONAL EATING

*'How does one become a butterfly? You must want to fly so much that
you are willing to give up being a caterpillar.' Trina Paulus*

*In this chapter you will:
learn how to combat guilty feelings around food and what you have eaten and let
go of the 'good/bad' food mindset
discover how to differentiate between emotional hunger and actual hunger
find out how to practise body awareness
learn how to use an ABC sheet instead of eating whenever you feel an emotional trigger,
or whenever you feel guilty or 'bad' about food choices and behaviours
understand the importance of practising well-being as a way of combating the need
to engage in emotional eating.*

Emotional eating is the main reason why people eat when they are not hungry. It's the tool we reach for in an effort to cover over or fill up a sensation of lacking. It is the symptom, not the cause, and it's important to understand this differentiation. We can, in so many areas of our lives, get caught up with our symptoms. But, as I always tell my clients, focusing on the symptom will only get you so far. In order to alleviate the symptom, you must address the underlying cause. If you feel emotional eating is a significant problem, then you may need to seek professional help to untangle and work through the underlying issues you are trying to cover over with food.

We cannot say all emotional eating comes from the same struggle. Everyone is singular, and therefore their relationship with food and how they use it is unique. Emma's journey articulates this entanglement very well: she struggled with emotional eating from a very early age and had been diagnosed with many different psychological and physiological disorders. She spent years working with various professionals focusing on her symptom, bingeing, to no relief. By the time she came to my clinic, she was despondent and depressed, eager to try and stop the bingeing, but I was not interested in her symptom. Instead I wanted to know about her: her personal story, her family relationships, her early interactions with other children, the formative experiences that shaped who she is, inside and out.

Through speaking, Emma uncovered that her insecurities stemmed from early comparisons with her sisters, who she described as skinny. This, coupled with a mother who was caught up in her own struggle with dieting, which she had inadvertently passed on to her daughter, led to a life-long obsession with food. Emma found that this was at the heart of her own personal struggle. While it seemed obvious once it was laid out in black and white, Emma had been focusing so much on what was wrong with her and the bingeing itself that she didn't stop to question how and why the

cycle of bingeing had begun in the first place. Early on, Emma's mother could see that the comparisons with her skinny sisters upset her daughter, so, with love and good intentions, she encouraged Emma to diet at a young age in an effort to save her daughter from the same struggle she had experienced. Thus the focus on weight loss, which actually reinforced a negative body image, originally came from a well-intentioned place, but inevitably had very damaging effects.

Through unearthing the family story around weight, Emma found that the symptom dissipated as she came to understand and work through the underlying emotional causes of her urges to binge. This client's story is, of course, complex, but what I hope to illustrate is that changing entrenched behaviours is absolutely possible. All that is required is the desire for change and a curiosity that leads to a questioning, which in turn opens up space for one's position to change.

As Emma often acknowledged, 'I never feel full when I'm eating due to emotional hunger.' This is because she wasn't hungry in the first place! So engaging in emotional eating typically leads to overeating, because you never get the message from your stomach to say that you're full. Emotional eating is a huge contributor to feeling unhappy with your body. In this chapter you will discover how to eliminate guilt from your food choices and how to recognise and overcome emotional eating for good.

Before we dive into addressing emotional eating, I first want to address something I hear my clients talk about all the time: guilt, or its other irritating nomenclature, 'being bad'. Uncovering how to eliminate guilt, or this constant push towards being 'good', is the first step in being able to address the deeper issues at play around food and your body.

I was out with some dear friends recently and one of our dinner companions was really struggling to enjoy the meal out, as she was on a diet and desperately trying to lose weight. She found ordering difficult, opting for the salad and skipping the starter, while the rest of us enjoyed the fabulous choice of fresh home-grown offers on the menu. By the time it came to dessert, my friend seemed eager to leave, as she clearly couldn't enjoy the meal and did not want to sit around and watch as we indulged in some seriously tasty Irish cheeses and desserts.

Our dinner companion did not enjoy the meal. In fact, speaking with her after, she told me how difficult it was to be 'good'. She felt that it only seemed to work when she didn't socialise, avoided alcohol and banished all things 'bad' from the house. My dear friend was caught up in something I think we all can identify with: this oscillation between being 'good' and 'bad'. What is more concerning is that her mood and sense of well-being was tied to what she ate. So if she had a 'good' day she would feel happy with herself, and a 'bad' day would result in her feeling absolutely rotten, which would generally lead to more bingeing on the 'bad' stuff.

Action #1: Give up the guilt

Here are the strategies I advocate to combat the unnecessary guilt that comes from trying to be 'good' but inevitably ending up being 'bad':

1. Aim for balance

I have no time for this good/bad business. Enjoying a love of food and your body is all about balance. Move away from controlling or trying to constantly stave off foods you love. Listen to your body and eat what you want, when you want. Allowing yourself freedom with food actually has the opposite result to what you would imagine. Eating whatever you want removes the 'badness' and the reliance on willpower from the equation. This means you can enjoy food without attaching all these negative thoughts and feelings to it. When you do this, you are much less likely to overindulge and binge. Feeling freedom around food means you're more likely to eat one cookie instead of the whole tin.

This was the first instruction I gave my client Emma. She was very sceptical at first and felt quite nervous, as she worried that this 'permission' meant that she would eat everything around her. But the opposite actually happened. By giving herself permission to eat whatever she wanted, with absolutely no restrictions or caveats, she relaxed around food. It stopped being constantly on her mind, as she found that she could actually enjoy whatever she wanted. She didn't overindulge, and the urge to binge just wasn't there. So many of my clients have had the same initial reaction of fear, as it is the exact opposite of what we are encouraged to do when we have issues around food and with our weight. But it really does work. Try it for yourself and see!

2. When you do overeat or indulge, then make sure to compensate the next day

This is a continuation of my first point on balance. When you do eat out and enjoy a scrumptious three-course meal, or if you find that you have engaged in emotional eating or bingeing, then you should compensate the next day by eating lighter foods, like a soup for lunch and a salad for dinner, and avoid the sweet treats for a day or so. I'll discuss this in more detail in Chapter 12, but this approach will help with the fixation on being 'good' and 'bad', by automatically viewing your eating habits from a position informed by 'balance'.

3. Use the rule of halves

Halve anything you want to eat, especially sweet treats. This will immediately help prevent any guilt from rearing its ugly head. If you want to eat a sweet treat or dessert, go ahead, but halve it before you even start to eat it. I have, and have always had, a very sweet tooth, and love cakes and treats. Baking is as relaxing to me as a bubble bath and a glass of champagne – seriously! So in order to feel freedom with the good stuff, I halve everything and give away, put away or, if it's not salvageable, throw away, the other half. The rule of halves is so simple and powerful. All the flavour is in the first few bites

anyway, so eating slowly and consciously will allow you to eat less, enjoy more and stave off any guilt or need to be 'good'.

4. Do an ABC sheet

(I will explain exactly what I mean by an ABC sheet later in this chapter so be patient!).

Isn't it time you stopped beating yourself up about food and your body? Ask yourself, how is this serving me? Is it helping me to achieve my goal: to feel comfortable and confident in my own skin? Practise these strategies, and if you do find yourself bingeing and feeling guilty afterwards, immediately do the ABC worksheet, as it will help dispel the guilt. I know you'll love it!

Emotional eating

Emotional hunger can occur when we're feeling low, stressed, disappointed, frustrated, angry, anxious or even bored. The biggest problem with emotional eating is that it doesn't make you feel better, less bored, whole or happy. Unfortunately, it has the exact opposite effect and actually makes you feel worse, as after eating something due to an emotional trigger, you end up feeling guilty and frustrated with yourself. The first step towards eliminating emotional hunger is to recognise it. The more you practise tuning in to your body, the easier it will be to identify emotional hunger.

Emotional hunger is a sudden, impulsive feeling, whereas actual hunger is gradual and doesn't become urgent until you are starving.

Typically, when you are hit with an urgent pang for a particular food, then some emotional trigger is involved.

The second distinctive characteristic that will help you distinguish between emotional and physical hunger is the fact that emotional hunger cannot be satiated with food. When you eat as a result of an emotional trigger as opposed to a physical trigger, you will find that you can continue eating without feeling full. This is when you end up eating a whole packet of biscuits without feeling satisfied.

Food cannot fulfil the emotional deficit that you are experiencing, so while we experience emotional hunger in an urgent way, physical hunger is a very gradual feeling that builds up. Initially it will feel like a gentle message from your stomach, which, if you ignore it, can develop over time into a growling sensation. If you ignore this, hunger can then be experienced as a light-headedness, and eventually we can feel an emotional response to hunger: we can feel sad, or grumpy and tired. So it's important to pick up on your body's messages when you start to feel hungry. Remember the hunger scale:

start eating between three and four, hungry and slightly hungry, and you should aim to stop eating around six, pleasantly satisfied. Unlike emotional hunger, physical hunger is easily satiated, and once you eat something the feeling of hunger is replaced by a feeling of fullness.

ACTION #2: HOW TO OVERCOME EMOTIONAL EATING

PRACTISE BODY AWARENESS

The most important thing when it comes to addressing emotional hunger is awareness. We have become so alienated from our bodies that we tend to drown out the subtle messages it sends us. It is essential that you relearn how to listen to your body. Take a moment now and look back over the food journal you recorded during discovery week:

How much of what you ate occurred when you weren't actually hungry?

How much of what you ate occurred because food was offered to you or available?

How much of what you ate occurred due to emotional eating? (Eating because you were bored, stressed, sad, fed up, angry, happy and so on, or just feeling a bit empty and looking to fill that void.)

What's the ratio of food you ate because you were hungry or because of the reasons listed above? I know this is hard to calculate, but are you surprised at the amount you ingested that had nothing to do with fuelling your body?

Practise body awareness now: place your attention in your body; now attune your attention towards your stomach. Are you hungry for food at this moment? Where do you feel you are on the hunger scale?

Every single time you're about to put food in your mouth ask yourself, 'Am I hungry? Where do I feel I am on the hunger scale? What am I hungry for?'

Emotional hunger is a very different feeling. As I've said, if you feel a sudden pang of hunger, often for a particular food, then an emotional trigger is probably involved. So many people turn to food in an effort to cover over deeper psychological issues. Whenever you feel yourself getting anxious, sad, bored, upset or are experiencing pangs of emotional hunger, I have a very effective exercise to help you. It's called an ABC sheet. My clients absolutely love this tool and find it extremely helpful in addressing emotional hunger.

HOW TO ADDRESS 'EMOTIONAL HUNGER' TRIGGERS

Do an ABC sheet.[1] This is a commonly used

cognitive behavioural tool and I encourage you to use it whenever you feel guilty about food, or if you are feeling anxiety or dissatisfaction with your body. You must physically go through the exercise in written form. Once you see your thoughts written down, you will realise that they are just ideas or theories rather than actual facts. It only takes a couple of minutes and will help address the guilt you feel. So whenever you feel a pang of guilt (or indeed any toxic thought), immediately take the time to do a worksheet.

What you think determines how you feel, and this in turn directly informs your behaviours and actions. This tool will help you challenge and change the unhelpful thoughts at a conscious level, which will instantly help you feel more at ease in yourself. If you think about it, the more negative you feel, the more likely you are to perpetuate negative thoughts, and this can easily develop into a negative thought cycle. Use an ABC sheet whenever you feel upset or guilty, or when you have acted in a way that you are unhappy with and would like to change, like binge eating.

Start with the Consequences box. Take a minute to assess how you are feeling right now. This is the most logical place to start, as emotions and behaviours are consequences of the interplay between the activating or trigger event and the beliefs around them. See the examples below for suggestions.

Next, turn to the Activating/Trigger Event box. This can really be anything at all: use your feelings as a guide to uncover the activating event that triggered the negative thought spiral. Aim to focus on the specific aspect of the event that upset you. Rather than going into detail, try to be as succinct as possible and distil your thoughts.

Now look at the Beliefs box. What thoughts and attitudes do you have about the activating event that led to the emotions you wrote in the Consequences box?

Finally, turn to the Dispute box, which will help you reduce the intensity of the unhelpful thoughts by coming up with more supportive and positive ways of thinking and acting. This step is critical, as it is these alternative thoughts that will empower you to change your actions and feel more at ease in yourself. So take the time to write out more flexible and positive responses to every 'negative belief' you have written down. This process is extremely empowering and my clients absolutely love it!

A) Activating/ Trigger event	Write out what you think triggered your emotions: an event/ situation/sensation/memory
	(e.g. something that just happened, a past event, an event that will occur in the future, or that you fear will happen in the future; a person, place or thing that causes you distress; something within your mind, a thought or memory; your own emotions or behaviour or a physiological reaction, heart racing, shortness of breath, headache, tiredness, blushing, sweating, sudden pang of hunger).
B) Beliefs, Thoughts and Attitudes about A	Write out your thoughts, attitudes and beliefs about A, or what it meant to you.
	Beliefs can be about you, others, the world, your past or future.
	The beliefs may seem extreme or distorted and are typically very negative thoughts about yourself, the situation or others.
C) Consequences of A & B on your behaviours and emotions	Write out the emotions you are feeling
	(e.g. anger, anxiety, hurt, shame, guilt, disgust, depression, envy, hurt, jealousy, shame, sadness).
	How did you react to these emotions
	(e.g. overindulging in food or other substances, binge-eating or restricting food, avoiding or escaping the situation, withdrawing, isolating yourself, procrastinating, being aggressive or seeking reassurance or support)?

D) Dispute - Question and examine the beliefs and create alternative ways of thinking

Question and examine the beliefs and create alternative ways of thinking.

Dispute each negative belief with logic and evidence. Questions you can ask to prompt yourself are:

Is this thought logical or illogical?

Would others think this thought is extreme?

What evidence disproves this thought?

Is this thought caught up in my negative beliefs or is it actually based on reality and facts?

Can I prove that this thought is 100 per cent truthful?

(Do not simply answer 'yes' or 'no' to these questions. Consider them and generate alternative ways of thinking in response to the negative thoughts and beliefs.)

In order to come up with positive responses to the negative thoughts, ask yourself:

How can I look at this situation in a more kind and helpful way?

What would I say to a loved one who was thinking this way?

When I am feeling good in myself, do I think this way?

What life experiences have shown me that there is an alternative way of thinking about this?

What can I think in order to act and feel differently about A?

Your turn!

Remember to keep your answers as brief and as accurate as you possibly can.

Some thoughts and behaviours are more entrenched than others. It may take some time and effort, and many ABC sheets, to tackle the thoughts and behaviours that are weighing you down. By going through the exercise, you are, over time, changing and reprogramming your mind to think more flexibly. Essentially, you're learning how to challenge rigid negative thinking by opening up mental space to consciously acknowledge an issue and think about it differently. This is a powerful process that is directly applicable to your struggle with your attitude towards your body and your relationship with food. I encourage you to regularly use the ABC sheet. Start off using one once a day, as the better you get at the sheets, the more effective they become at interrupting the negative train of thought. The more you practise this exercise, the better you will become at addressing negative thinking (in this context, emotional eating and guilt around food). Practise will help change the negative behaviours and the unhelpful thought patterns behind them. Creating new ways of thinking and new helpful behaviours takes time and repetition.

As with overcoming guilt around food, the ABC sheet is a really useful tool you can use to work through and address the cause of your urge to engage in emotional eating. Once you recognise that you are experiencing the pangs of emotional eating, do not reach for the chocolate! Whenever you notice yourself feeling at that point where you want to eat for emotional reasons as opposed to feelings of actual hunger, do an ABC sheet, whether it be boredom, sadness, emptiness, stress, loneliness, anger or whatever the feeling is. As I said previously, and I cannot stress this enough, the key to it is that you must physically go through the exercise in written form. My clients often tell me that they have done a couple of ABC sheets and not found them terribly effective. I then ask if they went through the exercise in their head or if they wrote it out. Invariably they didn't bother to write out their answers and that's precisely why the exercise didn't work. Through writing out your answers you are focusing your mind and challenging your thinking, because when you see your answers written out they make a more profound impact. You can clearly review, amend and assess your thoughts, and it also gives you the opportunity to return to them and see the progress you are making over time.

Clients are always surprised at the difference when they redo the exercise in written form. The idea here is that you are interrupting the feelings, acknowledging and addressing them. This will help combat the need to fill the feeling with food.

I hope you are clear on how to differentiate between emotional hunger and physical hunger and you now have a powerful tool to use whenever you feel the pangs of emotional hunger. Over the next week I want you to really start to listen to your body and, every little while, tune in to where you are on the hunger scale. If you recognise that you're not actually hungry, don't eat! If you recognise that you are experiencing a craving due to emotional hunger then pull out a piece of paper and go through the ABC exercise.

WELL-BEING

I want you to get comfortable with the sensation of waiting to eat until you actually feel hungry, instead of giving in to a sudden urge to eat fuelled by some emotional trigger. I had a wonderful client, Lucy, who found that her struggle was not caught up in weight, but in her inability to face emotional issues that were surfacing. She had become accustomed to dealing with difficult emotions by bingeing on sweet things, ultimately making herself feel sick. Once she learned to differentiate between emotional hunger and actual hunger, she discovered that she could wait, sit with the emotional trigger, and acknowledge and address it, comfortable in the knowledge that she could eat when she next actually felt hungry. In learning how to do this, she managed to prevent two major pitfalls that are typically the consequence of emotional eating: she managed to avoid both bingeing and the unsavoury guilt that always accompanies it.

Lucy's compulsive behaviour was replaced by a new-found understanding that she needed to love and respect her body. Her way of achieving this came in the form of self-care, a concept she had struggled with in the past. Lucy had grown up in a busy home where everyone was expected to pull their weight, so having personal time or relaxing was not privileged (I can absolutely relate to this and indeed still find it hard to 'relax' at times!). So as an adult Lucy struggled to do nice or kind things for herself. I've said this many, many times so far, and indeed you will no doubt hear me say it again: the essence of accomplishing the Artful Eating philosophy is loving and respecting yourself, inside and out. Everything else stems from there. This will help with the emotional issues you are swallowing down with food, which will help with finding other ways to reward yourself and feel pleasure, which will help with having more energy and vitality. So please take it seriously!

The latest research on the topic of emotional eating indicates that the feeling of inescapable stress is a major factor.[2] We experience stress for all sorts of reasons: a bad relationship, a difficult boss, feeling overwhelmed, an ill family member or a chronic illness. You have heard me speak before about the cause of your weight gain or the cause of your unhappiness with your body, and the chances are that these emotional factors are negatively impacting your life and leading to emotional eating. I devoted the whole of Chapter 8 to this, so I won't say too much more at this point, only to mark it and recognise that mental and physical well-being are an important contributor to overcoming emotional eating. Remember to address your emotional needs. How well are you sleeping? As you have learned, sleep deprivation causes weight gain, as does stress, because the hormones produced by lack of sleep and stress not only interfere with hunger signals but also affect your metabolism. So it is extremely important that you start to privilege a good night's sleep! Also remember to practise meditation, as it is a wonderfully effective way of reducing stress, another major contributor to emotional eating. Develop a routine that prioritises both sleep and daily meditation as much as you do other aspects of your health and well-being. What I am advocating here is focusing on creating healthy conditions, which will help to eradicate the causes that underpin your emotional eating.

FOOD AS YOUR ONLY SOURCE OF PLEASURE

I often ask my clients what they would feel if they did not binge or overeat, and the common answer is, 'I would have nothing to look forward to.' I can understand that at the end of a long, challenging day, a sweet treat or a glass of wine can be especially effective in temporarily giving pleasure. Why? According to many sources, eating sugar and fat releases opioids in our brains.[3] Opioids are the active ingredients in cocaine, heroin and many other narcotics. So the calming, soothing effects you feel when you eat ice cream and biscuits are real, and breaking these habits can feel like overcoming a drug habit. But there are other ways of feeling pleasure and relaxation.

Lucy managed this transition so well. For a long time she had been hiding her bingeing and allowing the negative emotions to determine how she experienced her days. But through questioning her behaviour and focusing on 'waiting', she found the mental space to start to look outwards to the world around her. She became more curious and more adventurous. She took up lots of fun activities and engaged more socially and in the workplace, and these activities also resulted in a positive chemical response in the brain. Sure, she had been doing some of these things before, but not with the same energy and enthusiasm. She also finally learned the value and effectiveness of self-care: taking care of her body, regularly getting a massage or facial, getting her nails done, buying nice things or spending her money on wonderful experiences.

Now this may seem like an indulgence or a luxury, but think about the message you are sending yourself: I love and respect my body and I take care of myself. When you take care of yourself you automatically feel better, both physically and mentally. This in turn makes you behave in a more nurturing way and helps to alleviate the urge to engage in emotional eating. As part of your approach to overcoming emotional eating, it's time to start finding other ways to reward and soothe yourself besides food. Initially it's possible that these alternatives won't be as effective as eating the sweet things, but they will help fill the void where the unhelpful behaviour once was.

ACTION #3: FIND OTHER WAYS TO REWARD AND SOOTHE YOURSELF BESIDES FOOD

Here are some ideas to de-stress and feel good after a long day:

- *have a shower while listening to your favourite podcast (this is my go-to relaxation method and I do it every evening after work)*

- *brush your teeth (not terribly soothing, but it defiantly eradicates the desire to eat!)*

- *drink a fruit-flavoured tea or add fresh fruit to your water*

- *do your nails*

- *do a face mask*

- *read a glossy magazine*

- *organise your papers, wardrobe or jewellery*

- *ring a friend for a chat*

- *watch your favourite TV show*

- *go for a walk*

- *do some online 'window shopping' (I love this!)*

- *read a good book*

- *meditate.*

Any other suggestions?

PRACTISING BODY APPRECIATION

Another major trigger for emotional eating, and one I see emerge time and again with my clients, is having negative feelings towards your body. Now this may sound counterintuitive, but it's true: hating your body is a significant contributor to emotional eating. Negativity, shame and hateful thoughts simply cannot inspire you to treat your body with respect or commit to long-lasting changes and positive choices. So many of my clients tell me they will stop hating their body after they achieve their goal weight. But as I have said previously, it is so important to feel good in your body *now*. Indeed, so many of my clients tell me that they are no longer interested in physical intimacy with their partner, or they put off meeting someone special, either consciously or unconsciously, because of their dissatisfaction with their body. In order to overcome all the negative behaviours around food, you must respect your body before you can stop the emotional eating cycle. With this in mind, every morning I want you to focus on five things you like about your body, and feel the good feelings and gratitude for the bits you do like and can appreciate. You can incorporate this task into your 'ten thankful things' daily ritual. You may find this difficult at first, but with practise it will become easier – as with all things I advocate!

ARTFUL EATING

DESSERT

CONFIDENCE AND CREATIVITY IN THE KITCHEN

'You don't have to cook fancy or complicated masterpieces –
just good food from fresh ingredients.' Julia Child

In this chapter you will:
discover how easy and satisfying it is to make things from scratch
get acquainted with the basics, helping you become a competent and confident home cook
discover the magic of falling in love with food and flavours
find out why there is no 'one-size-fits-all' meal plan or prescriptive approach to
eating artfully
discover the importance of making a meal of it!
find out how to enjoy entertaining.

During my early attempts at 'playing house', my friends knew to line their stomachs before coming to dinner, as inevitably my experimentation would fall short of my hopes. (Think Bridget Jones's inedible blue soup.) Yet I continued to try and fail many times. The problem was that I hadn't mastered the basics and, if I'm honest, I was too impatient.

I didn't feel confident or happy in the kitchen. Learning how to bake has helped immensely, as baking teaches the art of patience, something my husband constantly reminds me I need to improve upon (patience, not baking). I think both patience and confidence are the best ingredients for any decent meal, followed closely with a sprinkle of pleasure and a good dollop of love.

I suspect my love of cooking was there from a very early age, though it didn't quite have the chance to blossom until I had my own kitchen. As a child I loved making things, like a puppet theatre from a cornflakes box or a tree house from old wooden pallets. I would write poetry, songs, paint abstract pictures and create secret hiding places in my bedroom with curtains and sheets. I was constantly 'making and doing'. The important point, however, is that nothing I made was ever really very good! I wasn't a great artist or poet. My parents certainly didn't fawn over my creations and marvel at my ingenuity. Even their love couldn't rose-tint my mediocre attempts at artistry. But none of that mattered to me, because I enjoyed the process. I was happiest attempting to make something, salvaging and sourcing the things I needed from the unlikeliest of places (I was a child of the eighties, growing up in the countryside, so finding sellotape and a pair of scissors was often a challenge).

The point though was that I was not a slave to perfection. If I had been, I'm sure I wouldn't have attempted to make anything. I had this same yen for creativity in the kitchen, much to the chagrin of my mother, who incidentally is a wonderful cook. I would, and still do, make an awful mess. Even as a child I would attempt the art of substitution, as often I would try to make things that we only had half the ingredients for. Unfortunately, I still haven't found a substitute for eggs, so I do my best not to run out of these. I think this attitude served me well and today is still the approach I take to cooking. My motto, with all things in life, is 'good enough'. I have borrowed this phrase from a wonderful psychoanalyst, Donald Winnicott, who coined the term 'the good-enough mother', which according to his theory was the optimal way for a mother to be. Within the context of parenting, when the parent is not a perfect, omnipresent figure in the infant's life, not rushing to their every need instantly but gradually allowing space for slight frustrations, it is extremely healthy for the infant's development. This is a complex theory, but what I take from it is that perfection, in anything, isn't always the ideal to strive for. We are human and need to allow for the exigencies of normal life; thus the good-enough mother is a sentiment I carry throughout my life and it gives me the confidence to attempt all sorts of things, knowing that I need not try to strive for perfection. Indeed, I encourage you to acquire this motto, not just in the kitchen, but in all aspects of your life. Most especially in the way you approach Artful Eating!

I fully embraced cooking in my late twenties when my sister Alana, my then boyfriend (now husband) Liam and I bought my grandfather's house. As it was always affectionately called, 147 had a large, sunny, south-facing kitchen that looked out onto a sixty-foot-long garden. This garden had a wonderful legacy. It provided enough food to feed my father and his ten sisters. (Yes, ten!) My grandfather Alfie had incredible green fingers and he grew absolutely everything. The garden, to me as a child, was a magical place. Gramps would bring us there to pick flowers, tomatoes, asparagus and courgettes, and he would always send us home with bags filled to the brim with fresh, earthy vegetables and flowers. I used to love nothing more than pulling the carrots out of the ground and eating them 'à la Bugs Bunny' with the green shoots still intact.

When we moved into Gramps' house, I was acutely aware of the legacy we were inheriting, so Liam and I, with a lot of help from my father, committed to continuing the tradition. I still remember that first year: it was incredible! We grew courgettes, tomatoes, corn, spinach, broccoli, potatoes, rhubarb, peas, carrots, onions, garlic, all sorts of herbs, rocket, lettuce and strawberries. I was amazed at what that garden produced. Having moved a few times since, I really appreciate the alchemy of that soil, the southern orientation and the fact that the drainage was exceptional. We just haven't been as successful since.

With this abundance of fresh, organic food, I began to really enjoy cooking and experimenting. I made preserves, jams, relishes, passatas, sauces, soups and all sorts of lovely dishes. With our large kitchen, I began entertaining and loved having boisterous dinner parties with friends and family, because I so enjoyed sharing the fruits of our labour. Looking back now, it was a really wonderful, carefree time. I'm smiling as I remember it . . . It's really when I learned to cook and I enjoyed it so much. This is what I want to pass on to you, if you don't already feel this way about cooking. I've worked with lots of clients who, when it comes to this point in the Artful Eating process, profess that they cannot cook, they don't enjoy it and they don't have a very adventurous palate.

A wonderful client of mine comes to mind, Claire. A young mum, she and her partner both worked so didn't have a lot of free time, especially with a little one to take care of. Claire was in a bit of a food rut. She wasn't into cooking, she admitted she wasn't a big vegetable eater, and she certainly had never baked or attempted to make anything beyond pasta dishes or pre-prepared oven dinners. It took some persistent encouragement on my part, but she started with the basics: home-made soup, filled with nourishing vegetables and absolutely no added nonsense. I remember her telling me how good it tasted and how much she enjoyed the process. Claire had been bitten by the bug! Over time she became more comfortable and confident in the kitchen. She noticed how her shopping patterns changed as she stopped buying ready-made meals altogether. Claire found that she managed to carve out the time to cook and prepare lunches and dinners for the week. She noticed how this new diet of home-made, nourishing foods left her with more energy, and helped her to lose weight! Over the space of a few months she went from nervous novice to someone who had turned to cooking and baking as a source of relaxation and pleasure. If you're not already there, this is what I want for you too.

To really experience the benefits of the Artful Eating philosophy, you have to get comfortable cooking from scratch. Learning to cook is like learning a new language: you have to master the basics first, and once you have them down, you can move on to more complex constructions. Also, when learning a new language, patience and time are necessary ingredients. So approach cooking with this in mind. It may be challenging at first, but once you become confident, you will experience great pleasure in using this new skill. I am not encouraging you to become a gourmet, but I just want you to understand how easy and satisfying it is to make things yourself. Sometimes you will get it wrong, and that is absolutely grand, but over time you will learn to master a couple of recipes. As I often say to my clients, confidence comes after you have achieved something, so give yourself time and patience.

WHY THERE IS NO 'ONE-SIZE-FITS-ALL' MEAL PLAN OR PRESCRIPTIVE APPROACH TO EATING ARTFULLY

At this point in any 'healthy-eating' tome there is typically a section where you are provided with a meal plan that lays out what you should eat for breakfast, lunch and dinner. Not so here. I know many of you reading this would find comfort in having a prescribed meal plan, but I just don't think it's a good idea. Thinking back to the four fundamental steps I laid out in Chapter 7 on 'how to eat', I advocate eating what you like and what you know you'll enjoy. Everyone's palate is different and people desire different things at different times, depending on all sorts of things: time, the weather, one's mood. Telling people exactly what to eat seems to me akin to telling people exactly what to wear – it's ludicrous. I want to empower you to trust yourself and have the confidence to listen to your body and eat what you want, when you want, as long as it's not overly processed!

HOW TO ENJOY COOKING FROM SCRATCH

Cooking from scratch is absolutely key for anyone trying to shift to a non-processed diet. Many of my clients tell me they don't have time and that they don't feel confident in the kitchen. I will return to the issue of time later on, but in an effort to address the second issue, confidence, simple recipes are always the best solution. They are usually easily adaptable, as you can often substitute one ingredient if you don't have it with something similar. They are quick to make and, with good-quality ingredients, the flavours speak for themselves. Simple recipes will definitely help grow your confidence and reinforce your resolve to cook more as you feel proud of your creations. Remember: positive associations breed repeated behaviours.

The starting point, however, is a few basic techniques.

You do not need to be an amazing gourmet; you just need to be able to feed yourself good-quality, unprocessed food on a daily basis. As I have already said, the most important piece is buying good-quality seasonal food and learning the basic skills you need to create something tasty. Once you commit to making cooking part of the fabric of your life, it will very quickly stop feeling like an ordeal and will become second nature. Your mindset in the supermarket will be 'I don't buy pre-prepared meals' or 'I don't buy overly processed foods'. This shift will happen very quickly as you discover just how wonderful it is to taste home-made creations.

In a very short time, you'll get faster at chopping, you won't need to check recipes and painstakingly measure out ingredients, and you'll intuitively know when and in what order to add things. But it does take practice, and opening a fridge and knowing what goes well with what can only come from trial and error. You need to discover for yourself what tastes you like. One of the most important tips is to taste as you cook. Always test the flavour of your food, as you will know innately what flavours you enjoy.

Get acquainted with the basics. For some of you this may be too basic, but for others this is exactly where you need to start. I want to impress upon you the idea that home-cooked food can be fast food. I'm going to share some very simple techniques for cooking that are quick, easy and make uncomplicated, delicious food. When you're using the best quality you can source, let the ingredients speak for themselves.

To steam

Bring 1 cup of water to a boil in a large pot and place a steaming basket or pot over the water and cover it with a lid.

Chop your vegetables of choice. You don't have to be precise here, and the size to which you chop them depends on how you would like them. The larger they are chopped, the longer it will take for them to cook. When steaming vegetables, I like to cut them into bite-sized chunks. Do not overcook them; they should maintain their vibrant colour and be crunchy to taste after steaming.

Once cooked, add a dollop of butter or a drizzle of olive oil for flavour. You can season to taste and sprinkle with fresh or dried herbs, or a squeeze of lemon, or even a sprinkle of seeds if you fancy. You can cook most vegetables this way. Steaming is often overlooked or considered a 'diet' option, but I adore steamed vegetables on their own or as a foundation to all sorts of dishes. There is also a lot of research that supports the idea that briefly steaming vegetables helps to preserve vitamins, minerals and antioxidants.[1]

To sauté

Like many little girls, I was an aspiring ballerina,

so for me to sauté meant to jump off both feet and land in the same position! Now it has a very different meaning: to fry food quickly in a little hot fat.

Chop your vegetables of choice. Heat 1 tablespoon of extra virgin olive oil or coconut oil over a medium-high heat in a large frying pan.

Once the pan is hot, add the vegetables and sauté for 5 to 7 minutes, stirring occasionally until they are cooked to your desired level of tenderness. Be careful not to overfill the frying pan; there should be enough room for all the food to touch the bottom. If you like, add some garlic, onions and my favourite, mushrooms, to sautéed vegetables to make a wholesome dish.

You can sauté fish or chicken in the same way.

COOKING FISH AND CHICKEN

Fish and chicken are easy to prepare in delicious and healthy ways. Just grill, broil or sauté fish or chicken, then season with any (or a mixture) of extra virgin olive oil, a drizzle of lemon juice, fresh or dried rosemary, fresh garlic or ginger, or coriander. When you have fresh fish (I am very careful when it comes to fish; try and eat ethically sourced fish, not farmed) or a delicious, organic free-range chicken breast, let the flavour speak for itself. There really is no need to overcomplicate unless you're in the mood and have the time to try something more extravagant – in which case, pull out your favourite cookbook and get creative!

To grill

Place the grill rack over the grill pan. Season the fish or chicken with whatever you fancy; with chicken I sometimes opt for cayenne pepper for a kick, or a drizzle of lemon for something zingy.

The fish should be cooked until it is tender and opaque throughout; this should take approximately 7 to 10 minutes. Turn the fish over just once, halfway through.

Chicken will take longer to cook, perhaps about 15 minutes. Turn it halfway. It's ready when it is firm to touch and white throughout. Always cut into the centre of the breast to check it's cooked through.

To roast

Preheat the oven to approximately 240°C/ Fan 220°C/Gas 9 and make sure it's hot and then turn it down to 200°C/Fan 180°C/Gas 6 when you put the food in. Chop the vegetables and place them in an ovenproof dish; again, be mindful not to overcrowd the dish. Drizzle with olive oil, season with sea salt flakes and freshly ground black pepper, and add whatever herbs you fancy. You could also add a dash of balsamic vinegar to roasted vegetables. All vegetables roast well, but I particularly adore roasted butternut squash and roasted parsnips. The latter I like to douse in either honey or maple syrup.

If I'm roasting a fillet of fish or a chicken breast I like to make up a little parcel of herbs, maybe add a squeeze of lemon and a knob of butter or olive oil, and loosely package it in a tinfoil or parchment pouch, one piece of fish or chicken per parcel. This keeps all the juices and flavours intact. I'll then serve it up in the parcel with some boiled potatoes (perhaps boiled with some fresh sprigs of mint or rosemary), so the juices flow onto the dinner plate and get soaked up by the potatoes. This is really basic, easy, fast food, but honestly healthy and tasty. So much better for you than a bowl of pasta and a jar of store-bought sauce!

HERBS AND SPICES

As I am encouraging you to eliminate all processed foods, herbs and spices will become central to your cooking technique. Get tasting and find out which combinations you like. This will come from smelling, tasting and experimentation. It's great to have fresh herbs to hand and I always have a variety of herbs growing in my garden. If you don't have a garden, a windowsill will easily substitute. If you're planning on growing your own, don't start with the pots bought from the supermarket. These are often force-grown and the pots are overfilled, so I find they never last very long. Either grow from seed or buy herb pots from a garden centre, which have a much better chance of thriving.

I prefer using fresh herbs where possible, but dried herbs and spices are fantastic too. Add fresh rosemary, chopped fresh coriander, or fresh crushed garlic or fresh sliced ginger to your vegetables. Herbs also have incredible detoxification benefits. You could try placing a couple of slices of ginger in the water while you're cooking rice or add a couple of teaspoons of turmeric to make Indian-style yellow rice. Both ginger and turmeric are powerful anti-inflammatories, and it's a bonus that they give the rice a delicious aroma and flavour. Occasionally I'll add turmeric and ginger to my warm lemon water for a breakfast-time boost.

PREPARE MEALS FROM SCRATCH AS OFTEN AS POSSIBLE

On your journey to becoming a competent and confident home cook, I encourage you to cook often. Practice does indeed make perfect and the more often you cook the more accomplished you will become. If you are a complete novice, try carving out 'cooking days', perhaps three days a week. Incorporating cooking into your weekly routine will allow you to plan ahead and make sure you have the things you need.

PREPARE FOOD YOU'LL ENJOY EATING

Remember step 3 of 'how to eat' in Chapter 7? Eat what you want and enjoy it. This goes for cooking too! Often people who aren't comfortable cooking attempt a 'healthy' recipe in an effort to eat better, or an extravagant recipe because they like the look of the picture, or they want to impress their dinner guests. This is a big mistake and can put you off the joys of cooking. Start out by preparing things you know you'll enjoy. When you make food that you like the taste of, it's likely that your family or dinner companions will enjoy it too. Their ensuing praise and the pleasure you experience create positive associations with your home cooking, which will reinforce your desire to cook.

USE THE RIGHT TOOLS

The right tools can save you a lot of time, especially when it comes to the most basic techniques: chopping, sautéing and flipping something over in the pan. A sharp knife is probably the most essential tool you can have in the kitchen. Once you experience a properly sharpened knife, you'll understand, on a deeper level, how important it is to use the correct tool for all your kitchen tasks. Check the recipe section for my basic kitchen tools list.

MAKE A MEAL OF IT

Even if you are just eating for one, make a meal of it. Lay the table elegantly, with a napkin and maybe some flowers or a candle. These are powerful cues that are sending the message 'enjoy'. We all know we shouldn't eat standing up or while watching TV. Take your time and use your meal as a period of relaxation and pleasure. The anticipation has been building while you have been cooking, so sit down and consciously enjoy the food you've made. For example, if I make a soup, I always garnish it. It's these little touches of indulgence that make all the difference. I do think that what the food looks like matters as much as how it tastes. We eat with our eyes, so get creative and make sure the food looks appealing. You will enjoy it more and you will have fun creating beautiful plates of food. The dishes and cutlery you use are important too, so invest in some beautiful dinnerware. It doesn't have to cost a fortune; you can buy it in the sales or second hand on eBay.

Also think about serving up the food in courses as opposed to piling it all on one plate. For example, if you're having a salad with your meal, why not serve it first and let the main dish follow? Each of my meals is served in courses; this means I will eat more slowly. It's also a great ruse, as I'm fooled into thinking I'm eating more than I am. By having lots of little courses, you get variation, you can savour each of the flavours, you can eat more slowly, and you won't feel the need to pile up your plate. An example of this might be soup and bread, followed by a hearty salad with boiled egg and feta, followed by a piece of fruit sliced and presented nicely with some cheese, or some natural yogurt and crushed pecans, or coffee with a gourmet chocolate or artisan biscuit.

BE A CURIOUS AND ADVENTUROUS EATER

As I've already mentioned, I work with so many clients who are fixed in their eating habits and have quite a limited palate. But you simply can't learn how to be a competent cook unless you're an open-minded eater. This is something that may be challenging for some, but I am always delighted when I see my clients push themselves beyond their comfort zone with foods and flavours. The results are so rewarding! Try things, be curious and understand that developing your food palate takes time and a desire to change. I used to hate tomatoes; I really can't believe it now, but when I was young I couldn't stand the taste of them! As I got older I recognised how limiting this was and so forced myself to eat them, with a drizzle of olive oil and some sea salt flakes. The texture and flavour took a bit of getting used to, but I developed a taste for them. Just as when we have our first sip of wine or beer, we may not like the flavour at first, but indeed we persevere!

I want you to do the same with foods. If you are curious and adventurous, this will permeate throughout your family too. If you have picky eaters in your family, make this transition to non-processed foods a positive one. Get them involved, and encourage their help to choose and prepare what to cook. Depending on their age, get each member to contribute a different element of the meal. You want to foster positive attitudes to and associations with this new approach to food, so bring your family along with you. Ask for their help, support and encouragement. You will all benefit from a healthier approach to eating.

THE IMPORTANCE OF FALLING IN LOVE WITH FOOD AND FLAVOURS

To really acquire the ability to easily cook from scratch, you must fall in love with food and flavours. This must be a pleasurable part of your life that you enjoy. Learning to appreciate good-quality produce and delicious dishes makes cooking a delight as opposed to a chore. So take an interest in where your food comes from; get to know your butcher, greengrocer and cheesemonger. Go to farmers' markets and talk to the people who make the produce; their enthusiasm and passion will enlighten and educate you. They will have lots of great tips and recipes that they love sharing. Watch cooking shows of chefs who inspire you. My absolute favourites are Nigella Lawson, Rachel Khoo, Nigel Slater and Mimi Thorisson; their passion for food is infectious. A glorious rainy Sunday in my house involves pulling out one of their cookbooks, choosing a recipe, sourcing the ingredients, putting on some music, and filling the house with delicious smells and flavours.

HOW TO ENJOY ENTERTAINING

Entertaining can be something we get quite stressed about, but it really doesn't need to be. The key to a successful dinner party is to create a warm and welcoming ambiance. Be attentive to your guests and make sure they have enough to eat and drink. Create a playlist of music to accompany your evening and have the table beautifully set with flowers and candles. This will go a long way to creating an inviting atmosphere that will entice your guests to feel at ease.

Forget about trying to make something extravagant or impressive. Ideally you should serve something that you can make in advance, like a curry or a roast, instead of something that needs to be prepared when your guests have arrived. Simple beats fussy every time, so cook something that you're comfortable with to start. If you are still preparing when the guests arrive, let them help! I find that giving your guests little tasks to do creates an informal atmosphere and helps them feel at home.

Have aperitifs to offer as your guests arrive; this is a lovely way to welcome people and put them at ease. My cousin who lives in France introduced me to the concept with a kir and I was hooked. A kir is a glass of white wine and a dash of crème de cassis (which is incredibly simple to make if you have a glut of blackcurrants). Make it a kir royale by swapping out the white wine for champagne: indeed, champagne is the perfect l'apéritif! It elevates a simple meal into something magical. My husband's current favourite is a variation on the Aperol spritz: instead of the Italian favourite of three parts prosecco, two parts Aperol and one part soda, try pouring two parts Aperol, one part sweet vermouth, then top with sparkling water over ice and garnish with a slice of orange. The glass matters for this one, so try to use a decent old-fashioned! Alongside the drinks, which at this point in the evening are the star of the show, offer something to nibble. This can be as simple as some crudités (sliced raw vegetables) with a bit of hummus if you wish, or some sliced charcuterie.

Soup is always a good starter, as it can be made beforehand. Serve it with some home-made brown bread. After your main, you can make a simple dessert: try Eton Mess, which is incredibly simple to make and looks fantastic in a wine glass with a sprig of mint. And finally, finish off with a selection of cheeses and crackers with coffee and of course a digestif: my husband loves a brandy, while I prefer a port, a perfect way to finish off the evening. So easy and enjoyable! I really encourage you to entertain at home: it is such great fun and very rewarding.

FAIL TO PREPARE, PREPARE TO FAIL

'What you do today can improve all your tomorrows.' Ralph Marston

'You will never find time for anything. If you want time, you must make it.'
Charles Buxton

In this chapter you will:
discover the importance of organisation for a productive kitchen
find out how to avoid waste by using your freezer effectively
prepare for the week ahead
learn how to save time and money without compromising quality or flavour.

A few years ago I was overwhelmed, juggling a fair few plates and feeling frazzled to say the least! One evening, seeing how overwhelmed I was, my husband put a particular Stones song on. Now I'd heard this song so many times, I'm sure we all have, but listening to it in that moment, late one night while I was desperately trying to multitask, something happened. Looking at Liam relaxing on the couch, I actually started to hear the lyrics, and it felt as if Mick Jagger was trying to tell me something . . .

Time is on my side . . .

I love this sentiment and I carry it with me everywhere now. It's as if recognising this fact had altered time: I now feel like I can squeeze more out of my day without feeling literally squeezed. This is the secret to my ability to be an organised person and get the things I need to do done, and it's especially important if you have little ones. In fact, I would say it is a necessity rather than something to strive for and so it's a sentiment I instil in all my clients. Your ability to plan and prepare when it comes to weight loss is an essential tool that will really help you move towards your weight-loss goal. If you don't have the right foods prepared in your cupboard or freezer, you will reach for something you think is convenient but may not actually be the best thing for you to eat. This leads to inevitable feelings of guilt and frustration. So preparing meals in advance and always having what you need on hand will prevent any unhelpful snap decisions.

ACTION #1: MAXIMISE THE USE OF YOUR FREEZER (30 MINUTES)

I cannot overemphasise the importance of utilising your freezer, as it will save time, money and facilitate your ability to always eat artfully. Inspired by my aunt Mary, whose freezer is an enviable delight, I now take my freezer organisation seriously, and so should you. She actually makes freezer organisation look pretty! If your freezer isn't organised, you will easily forget what you have.

Start by clearing your freezer out, assessing what you have and what you actually will use. It can easily become a dumping ground for things you think you'll use at a later time but have forgotten about.

Throw out anything that's been lingering in there too long and doesn't seem enticing to you.

When considering freezer use-by dates, keep in mind that dairy products and anything you have made will last for about three months when frozen. However, it does depend on the efficiency of your freezer and how fresh the food was when frozen.

Leftover dinners are perfect for freezing, but be mindful to freeze them in individual portions so you don't have to defrost the whole batch, just what you need. It's important to clearly label each meal with a name and date, so that you know what's what, as food can look very different when frozen.

Frozen vegetables will retain most of their nutrients as long as they are properly stored and frozen at their freshest. I like to wash, peel if necessary, and chop vegetables and immediately freeze them. It's a great idea to freeze fresh seasonal produce: broad beans, peas, cauliflower, carrots, broccoli, spinach and green beans all freeze very well. This way you can easily grab some to add to curries, soups, sauces or stews.

Every year consumers in industrialised countries waste almost as much food as the entire net food production of sub-Saharan Africa (222 million vs. 230 million tons).[1] I am very conscious of food waste, from an environmental perspective as well as from a financial perspective. As I am encouraging you to buy the best-quality

ingredients and always, where possible, source organic, it is essential that what you buy is used! I find fresh organic produce just doesn't last as long as non-organic, so prep and freeze what you're not going to use in the next day or two and you won't need to throw out rotten food.

Similarly, with fruit that's about to turn, peel, chop and freeze it. You can use it in a smoothie, or stew it to make a compote, jam or jelly. You can freeze sliced fruit and add it to water or cocktails, and it doubles up as ice cubes.

If you have a loaf of bread that you know won't be eaten before it goes off, slice it and freeze it and you can use it as toast or blitz it should you need breadcrumbs. Breadcrumbs are great for topping a pasta bake, making stuffing, or binding mince to make burgers, meatballs or vegetable burgers. They are also tasty if you dip a fillet of fish or a breast of chicken in egg and then cover with breadcrumbs and herbs for a flavoursome coating.

Yogurt and whole eggs unfortunately do not freeze well, but egg whites and hard cheese do. Whenever I go to France or Italy, I'll stockpile good-quality cheese, especially Parmesan, grate it and freeze it; that way I always have it to hand when cooking.

A favourite of mine is to freeze chopped ginger, garlic and chilli so it's ready to add while cooking.

When it comes to herbs that are about to turn, there are two things I like to do: either I freeze them in a bit of water in ice-cube trays, or I turn them into simple herb butters. You can mix soft herbs such as coriander, parsley or basil with soft butter and crushed garlic, wrap well in greaseproof paper, and freeze. Similarly, you can create flavoured oils by adding the herbs to ice-cube trays filled with oil. These are great to use straight from the freezer when cooking.

Finally, home-made stock is an essential freezer addition. Whenever I cook a roast chicken, I'll make stock with the leftover bones and freeze it. This makes a perfect and healthy base for soups, risotto, couscous or pasta sauce.

Now that you're clear on how to maximise the use of your freezer, there is absolutely no need for any food to go to waste. By planning and being organised you can ensure everything you buy is used, which will certainly save you money! Once you have space, it's time to get organised and prep for the week ahead.

SHOPPING EFFECTIVELY TO SAVE TIME AND MONEY

Ordering your food online is an excellent idea. It saves oodles of time and means you only purchase exactly what you need, which saves money as well. You can organise when to receive the delivery so that it can coincide with your weekly food-prep time. If ordering online isn't an option for you, then make a list before you go to the shop. Decide what you want to make for the week ahead and only buy what you need.

In an effort to cut down on waste, I encourage you to move beyond the habit of doing one big weekly shop. Just buy as and when you need it, especially with fresh produce. We tend to buy more than we need, and so much of the fresh produce ends up in the bin! Stock up on store-cupboard ingredients (tins of tomatoes, flour, rice, pulses and non-perishables) once a month.

ACTION #2: CARVE OUT TIME TO BATCH COOK EVERY WEEK (2 HOURS)

Every week I block off about two hours to prepare meals in advance for us to eat during the week. This may sound like a lot, but it means you'll make a big mess only once, and you will have everything you need conveniently available for the week ahead. We take time out to clean the house, do the washing or watch our favourite TV show, so managing to carve out time so that you and your family can eat healthily seems like a good idea to me! I love listening to music or a podcast and relaxing as I cook. This is time that slows down, as I enjoy creating and tasting. It most certainly isn't a chore. I feel this way because I know that we will have delicious food for the week.

Try as much as possible to use what's in season: it will taste better and be in optimal condition.

I usually cook up a large batch of about three different dishes and freeze them in individual portions; that way they are easy to reheat. One I'll do in the slow cooker. A favourite in my house is four-bean chilli (you can find this in the recipe section) and then I'll have something going in the oven and a few things on the hob. I also make a large batch of soup as part of preparing meals in advance for the week. In the summer, when I have a glut of tomatoes in the glasshouse, I'll make some simple passata and gazpacho (both freeze really well).

I'll typically make some hummus and maybe roast some peppers, which will last preserved in sunflower oil. Both hummus and the peppers easily jazz up a salad or open sandwich.

During my prep time I also pick and wash the salad, as this can be quite a time-consuming job, and it lasts a good few days in the fridge. I encourage you not to buy the pre-washed stuff from bags: it doesn't taste as good, and it's covered in chlorine and chemicals to keep it looking fresh, so it's not very healthy! Instead buy organic, unwashed salad and leaves. Fill your sink with water and a good dose of salt and let the leaves soak for a while. Dry them in a salad spinner and store them in your fridge.

Finally, I also prep my gorgeous green smoothie (see recipe section) ingredients by chopping everything up and freezing them in individual portions, so they are ready to whip out in the morning in no time.

I have thought about and prepared easy dinners, soups, lunch accoutrements and my breakfast gorgeous green smoothie, but perhaps the most important piece is always having something delicious and good to snack on! To that end, I also bake a lemon or courgette cake, or some scones, all of which freeze really well. I first slice the cake into individual slices so that I can pop it in the toaster if it takes my fancy.

My fridge always has natural yogurt, as I adore a little teacup of this with a glug of honey, crushed pecans and a tablespoon of oats. This is a quick snack that works for me any time of the day (though it is typically my breakfast staple). I suppose it replaces the bowl of cereal I would have snacked on in my youth!

Finally, always have your favourite fruit in a bowl somewhere visible. If you make a habit of reaching for a piece of fruit to snack on as opposed to a slice of toast or a biscuit, you will quickly start to notice the difference. I think it's really worth buying the best-quality fruit you can, as here you will certainly taste the difference. We are now very used to having our fruit in juice or smoothie form, but nothing beats the smell of peeling an orange. Eating fruit in its natural state takes time, tastes delicious and will really fill you up.

The idea here is that you should always have what you need to hand, and prep time should become an enjoyable part of the fabric of your week. Remember, time is on your side, and you will be surprised at how easy it is to prepare meals in advance. Once you commit to incorporating an activity into your life, there will always be time for it. Carve out a time that suits you, get prepping, and the following week you

will not miss a step as you have an abundance of the right foods to nourish you as you move towards your goal weight.

BALANCE

'How we live our days is of course how we live our lives.' Annie Dillard

In this chapter you will:
learn how to enjoy the foods you love without feeling guilty
understand how to incorporate sweet treats and alcohol into your diet without undoing all your great work
discover the power of quality and how it can really be one of the major tools that will help you easily achieve your goal weight
learn how to maintain the Artful Eating philosophy while on holiday or when your routine changes
address cravings and develop a way of managing them so they don't control you
explore questions that may have surfaced through your reading and application of the actions in this book.

Artful Eating is about balance in all things: life, food, exercise, health, pleasure, well-being. What I have tried to convey throughout this book is a sense that balance is at the heart of a happy, healthy relationship with food and your body: none of this restrictive nonsense, where whole food groups are eliminated, or extremist ideas about health and well-being are advocated. I'm a pragmatist and understand that incorporating new behaviours should be both manageable and sustainable. With the inevitable exigencies of life, this philosophy must be enjoyable and adaptable to suit who you are and where you are in your life right now.

The final piece of the puzzle, though indeed

I have been talking about it throughout the book, is *pleasure*. It's time to get your head around indulgence. In recent years there has been a big push towards 'clean eating': avoiding dairy, wheats, grains and sugars. This seems very extreme to me and the science shows that a healthy, balanced diet filled with a variety of foods is the optimal way of eating. What concerns me about the new 'clean eating' approach is that it reinforces this idea of being 'good' or 'bad', as people become obsessive about only eating 'clean' and then admonish themselves for giving in and having a croissant. To me, a croissant is a little piece of heaven and therefore can never be considered bad! So with this word 'balance' in mind, allow me to elaborate on my approach to indulgences and sweet treats.

UNDERSTANDING THE JOY OF PLEASURE AND INDULGENCE (IN MODERATION!)

We all need and deserve sweet treats and indulgences, and I absolutely adore them. In fact, I'm sure my enthusiasm for indulgences was at the heart of my motivation to develop the Artful Eating philosophy. I remember feeling despondent listening to my clients grapple with the latest diet that prohibited sugar or dairy; it just seemed so miserable to me. I grew up in a house where sweets and cakes were completely banned, as my parents could not enjoy a treat, they would have to eat the whole box! So I was never taught how balance and moderation go hand in hand with indulgence. If there was ever anything sweet in the house, it was devoured guiltily. Now I know many people advocate not having anything sweet in the house, because then it can't be eaten. But I disagree. As long as you enjoy it consciously, it is absolutely okay! The key is that it's about the quality of the flavour of the treat as opposed to the size. Remember, the flavour of anything is in the first few bites.

The bakery around the corner from my home is all natural and non-processed. They make these amazing chocolate brownies. I love them, but I recognise that a regular-sized portion is just too big. So I halve it and save the other half for my husband. I slice my half into three bite-sized chunks, and I make a cup of coffee and lay the brownie chunks out on a plate. I then savour each bite, chewing slowly and consciously enjoying it. It's a wonderful treat that I have at least twice a week, and I take the time to savour it, I do not gobble it down mindlessly (this is certainly not my only indulgence of the week by the way!).

As with all things, I again reiterate that it's about quality. One square of delicious organic quality chocolate is much more satisfying than a regular mass-produced chocolate bar. In fact, I would never buy sweets or mass-produced treats. I either make them myself or buy artisan excellent-quality treats to be savoured and enjoyed. I am reminded of how significant quality is as we've had lots of guests visiting recently to meet our darling daughter Claudia, who, as I write this, was born a few weeks ago. Everyone seems to bring something to eat, and over the weekend a dear friend brought a box of quality handmade Belgian chocolates from an artisan chocolaterie. They were delicious, a true indulgence, and we all wondered at their quality and taste. It was impossible to eat more than a few, as they were packed with flavour and substance. Another guest a day or two later brought a packet of biscuits. It was a well-known brand that would easily be found in anyone's cupboard, but I just couldn't eat them. They were highly processed and full of monosodium glutamate and all sorts of other rubbish, and even though I will admit I took a bite, they tasted horribly artificial and overly sweet to me.

This is the thing: like a wine lover who has honed their palate, you will find that by only eating quality sweet things, you will no longer like the artificial and overly sweet flavours of unhealthy cakes, biscuits and confectionary. This shift in itself will reduce the number of treats you eat. I simply couldn't buy, eat or enjoy the rubbish I once did. My clients agree, and I love hearing how they can comfortably walk into a service station without feeling the slightest pang to pick up a bar of chocolate or packet of sweets at the counter when once they would have almost certainly done so. They all say that they just have no interest. This is something you'll find too as you make this shift to privileging quality.

ENJOYING ALCOHOL

The same principle should be applied to alcohol. I recommend that if you do like a drink, try to limit your alcohol intake to mealtimes or drinking with some nibbles, as they do throughout mainland Europe. It is an accompaniment to a wonderful meal and should be enjoyed as such. Alcohol can be a real danger if we drink too much, as we tend to overeat or binge the next day. Alcohol lowers our inhibitions and affects our judgement, so be mindful of how much you drink. Try and buy the best wine you can afford and learn about the various grapes and varieties. Get educated about what you're drinking, experiment with different flavours, and try your hand at making some cocktails!

As with sweet treats, try good-quality drinks packed with wonderful flavours, and consciously enjoy them. You are now mastering the art of intuitive eating: that is, listening to your body, eating when you're hungry and stopping when you're full, and you can do the same with intuitive drinking. Be aware of how much you have had to drink. When you are drinking alcohol, sip and savour the flavour. Allow your taste buds to register the subtle notes of the drink, and always drink from an appropriate glass. I believe the glass you drink from is almost as important as the drink itself. My friends and family all laugh at me when I'm out, as the glass available will determine what I drink. I do enjoy a glass of craft beer, but only in the right glass, no Slim Jims or pint glasses, thank you. I like the Continental-style beer glass with a stem, and perhaps a slice of lemon in the beer: so refreshing! A glass or two of wine with any meal really makes it an occasion and should be regularly enjoyed. The slower you drink, the more time you will have to register the effects of the alcohol. It is a wonderful way to relax and wind down, but overindulging is not pleasant for anyone! Know and understand your limits with alcohol and learn to enjoy the amount that's right for you. Slow right down and also have a glass of still or sparkling water to sip while imbibing. Remember to think about balance: eliminating anything that you like from your diet will only lead to bingeing or falling off the wagon, and that is not what we want at all!

If you have opened a bottle of wine and know you're not going to finish it, don't worry, it will keep! To store the wine, replace the cork firmly and put it in the fridge. You can expect a full-bodied white wine to last up to five days when stored properly. Red wine will last three to five days, recorked and stored in a cool, dark place. For a lighter white or rosé wine, the life expectancy of a bottle that has been recorked and stored in the fridge is up to seven days. So do not feel the need to finish the bottle! I find it helpful to write the date I opened the bottle on the label so I know how long it will last in the fridge, otherwise I might forget. Wine is also great to store in the freezer for cooking. I decant it into a wide-brimmed jar and scoop out what I need, as I need it.

EATING OUT

I was out for a girlfriend's birthday recently. She had brought her gal pals from her gym, who I hadn't met before. They were a great bunch and we had a fantastic time, giggling the whole evening. These women were all very fit and healthy, as they are committed to a private training session they do four times a week together with a personal trainer. I noticed how they all ordered salads and avoided any sides. When it came to dessert they all automatically said 'no thank you', but I chimed in and said I'd love to see the menu. I decided to order the profiteroles and, with that, the tide had turned. It was as if my ordering had given them permission to enjoy a dessert too. I suggested we order two portions and all share. The profiteroles were truly delicious and everyone got to enjoy them without overindulging. This is something I strongly encourage. Eating in moderation and enjoying a little of what you like mitigates the inevitable binges that come from denying yourself the foods you love.

When eating out, order whatever you want! I always order a starter, main course and dessert, as I love eating a variety of flavours and tastes, and it's so enjoyable to have someone else do the cooking on occasion. However, I stick to the Artful Eating 'how to eat' steps: I eat slowly and enjoy every mouthful, and I never finish what's on my plate. It is important to leave room for the next course: think of that half-portion! I find it particularly easy to stick to the half-portion when eating out, and my clients agree. Just delineate half of the portion on your plate and only eat that much.

When eating out it is essential to be mindful of the hunger scale: you do not want to get to a point of feeling anything more than pleasantly satisfied. Remember that the flavour is in the first few bites. You must be able to enjoy eating out without the guilt of feeling that you have overindulged. Now, when it comes to dessert this is not something you should deny yourself. I always share my dessert with my dinner partner. That way I get to taste it and enjoy it, but not eat too much of it! My clients really marvel at this practical, balanced approach to eating out, as they find it so liberating. This is one of the major pitfalls that they would complain about; indeed, when trying to lose weight so many people would tell me how they would completely avoid socialising altogether. Not necessary! Now you have the coordinates to enjoy eating out and it's something I encourage, as it's an opportunity to put something nice on, feel good, and be nourished by good food, wine and conversation. Eating out, whether at an elegant restaurant or in a local coffee shop, is a privilege and a delight, so enjoy it!

CHANGING ROUTINES AND HOLIDAYS

My dear friend Chloe, every single summer, slims down in advance of her sun holiday. She works extremely hard to shift a significant amount of weight and, wow, is she disciplined. I always know when she has a holiday coming up, because her diet reduces to the bare minimum and the weight falls off. Then she goes on the holiday and completely splurges, giving herself permission to eat and drink to complete excess. Of course, she piles back on all the weight she

lost and, indeed, some more as well. This is the perfect example of how not to indulge, and I'm sure it sounds familiar to you!

The focus should be on pleasure, enjoyment and balance: something our friends in France and Italy have mastered wonderfully. I love holidaying in these countries, as I find their approach to pleasure and balance so inspiring. We can learn a lot from them. I spent my most recent holiday in the beautiful little French seaside town of Honfleur, which is an ancient fishing port with cobbled streets, and tall wooden buildings that sigh into each other. This is where the Impressionists came to paint *en plein air*. I've known about the place for a long time and it definitely didn't disappoint. I have to admit, though, that it takes me some time to truly wind down and relax on holidays. I'm not a great one for lying in; in fact, I'm almost always up at the crack of dawn. So finding my rhythm on holidays can be a struggle. Luckily my husband, Liam, is very good at taking it easy, and it's an art I greatly admire in him. The longer we are together, the more I begin to acquire some of these very important attributes. We are pushing close to a decade together now and I have managed to sleep in until 9 a.m. once or twice!

That is my predicament when it comes to holidays, but I know for so many people the build-up to going away and getting into the swimsuit or more revealing summer clothing can be extremely stressful. What I typically see is people desperately dieting and sticking to it, like my friend Chloe, because they associate more pain with getting into their swimwear and not feeling good in their skin than they do with denying themselves the foods they love. So once the tickets are booked, there is typically enough leverage there to motivate them to lose the weight. Does this sound familiar? But then you arrive at your destination and mealtimes become an important part of the holiday. Usually they're the only thing that punctuate the day and designate a rhythm, because holidays are all about relaxing, right? And so, having starved yourself to fit into the summer clothes, you now fall off the wagon and overindulge. All the hard work goes out the window, and typically you end up putting on more weight than when you began. Not good. Holidays can become a yo-yo disaster that your body will not thank you for. This is a good illustration of how we can completely lose sight of the joys of balance.

While in Honfleur, we stayed in a fourteenth-century townhouse with a winding wooden staircase and had breakfast brought to us each morning. What a sight! This was definitely breakfast 'French style', with baguettes, different types of pastries and croissants, *bien sûr*! I ate, enjoyed and savoured the warm, fresh breads. This is what France is all about for me. I adore croissants and I also love French baguettes — none of these supermarket 'baguettes' that you buy at home but the stuff fresh from a boulangerie, the texture of which is completely different: it's lighter, chewier and much less stodgy. Most importantly, it's delicious. Each morning, upon receiving this basket of beauty,

I was faced with a choice. Did I skip the carbs (which apparently should be forbidden, according to many weight-loss advocates)? Did I think, 'I'm on holidays I'll eat it all!' Or did I choose option number three: enjoy the food I love *in moderation*?

Each morning I enjoyed precisely half a croissant and a delicious, if small, piece of the baguette, and I savoured each bite, of course! However, later in the day when the bread basket came around, as it inevitably did for every meal, I was mindful that I had had my bread indulgence for the day and, mostly, politely declined the unnecessary filler and waited for the scrumptious main event.

The other pitfall of any holiday are those permission-giving thoughts that say, 'I'm on holiday, I can have that!' This is a big mistake: it's those impulse purchases of potato chips, ice-creams or cocktails that we ingest without really registering that tip the balance. When you are on holidays, and indeed at all times, think about balance. Think about trying new foods and flavours, and if you fancy a snack try some watermelon or a juicy orange. Whatever you do, notice and register what you are eating. Enjoy it and make it count. Eat the foods you love, but enjoy in moderation. I'm sure you have oft heard the expression 'the eyes are bigger than the stomach' and it is so true!

Going somewhere different is an opportunity to have a fresh perspective, to see and do different things and taste different flavours of life, not

just the culinary kind. My time in France this year gave me the mental space to reflect, to read, to enjoy a feast for the eyes, sightseeing throughout the beautiful seaside villages. It is also a wonderful time to get out and get moving. The weather is (hopefully) good and time is on your side, so take the opportunity to walk. Walk to as many places as possible. When I'm on holidays I regularly clock up more than 20,000 steps a day. You see more, and being more active helps a little to balance out the extra indulgences holiday time inevitably brings. Most importantly I had time to connect with my husband and enjoy our time together.

COMPENSATION

Life is all about balance, and it's important to listen to your body. The more you practice intuitive eating, the easier it will become, and very soon you will find that you do it automatically. But it does take conscious effort in the beginning. If you do have a heavy weekend, do not fret or feel guilty. You have not fallen off the wagon and all your good work has not come undone. Please do not catastrophise: this is not a diet, so you cannot go wrong. And I especially do not want to hear, 'I'll start again on Monday.' What rubbish! This is a way of life, and life, as I'm sure you know well, has ups and downs. So if you eat too much, or find that because your car broke down, or your child was sick, or your dog ate your homework, that you forgot to maintain the Artful approach, ordered a takeaway pizza and ate the lot, so what? The solution is so simple.

It's what you do consistently that shapes you, not what you do once in a while. Focus on being 'good enough': this, in my opinion, is much better than perfect (as I've said already in Chapter 10). Typically, at the weekend I enjoy a couple of glasses of wine, and I usually entertain or eat out, so there is an element of indulgence involved. If I have eaten lots of rich food, I will make the effort to eat lightly the following day to compensate. I might have a salad for lunch and soup for tea instead of a big dinner. There is no sense of deprivation involved, as I find that I'm just not that hungry, so it's easy to eat lighter for a day, and I'm happy to give my body a bit of a rest and nourish it with a hearty soup and simple salad. When you do overindulge, and you most certainly will, be kind to yourself: do not give into feelings of failure or guilt, simply remember to compensate and get on with enjoying your day. Starting again on Monday should forevermore be a distant memory as you enjoy a life of balance and freedom every day.

CRAVINGS

By now it should be obvious that I have a major sweet tooth, and I am well acquainted with craving something I fancy in order to treat myself, so it's important to have a strategy to address cravings when they do occur. The key is to understand and privilege moderation.

I encourage my clients to regularly indulge in a little of what they like. This absolutely helps to combat cravings, as you know you can have the thing you fancy when you are actually hungry.

Remember to indulge in just a little bit of it, as opposed to bingeing on the whole lot. This is easy to do when you use the hunger scale: eat when you're hungry and stop when you're full. By not viewing the thing you crave as 'bad', you will mitigate any guilt that would have been attached to eating it. Instead, enjoy it and feel good about treating yourself. Having this healthy relationship with sweet things means you will never overindulge, as there is no strait-jacket. My clients marvel at how this shift in mindset results in feeling freedom with food and flavours.

ACTION #1: HOW TO DEAL WITH CRAVINGS

With this in mind, when you do feel a craving (as you inevitably will):

- *Acknowledge it.*

- *Practice body awareness.*

- *If you are hungry, go ahead and eat it!*

- *If you aren't hungry, then know and trust that you can have it when you actually feel hungry.*

- *Use the power of 'I don't' and tell yourself, 'I don't eat "x" when I'm not hungry' or 'I don't eat "x" because it's a processed food'. (You'll be surprised at just how powerful this phrase is: try it yourself and see!)*

- *If the craving persists, do an ABC sheet to combat the craving.*

Alternatively, use these behavioural strategies to interrupt the craving and divert your thoughts. Take space from food by trying the following:

- *Get out of the kitchen and do something you enjoy.*

- *Make a cup of herbal tea or drink a glass of water.*

- *Brush your teeth.*

- *Do a face mask.*

- *Have a shower.*

- *Call a friend.*

- *If you have pets, spend a bit of time playing with them.*

- *Tidy your inbox.*

- *Peruse the Internet, read a blog you enjoy or do some internet shopping.*

- *Do some gardening.*

- *Relax: do something that brings you pleasure and takes your mind off the craving. For instance, my sister loves getting absorbed by a 3D jigsaw. It's not my idea of fun, but think about it: what's yours?*

Exercise is a great way to take your mind off a craving and also curbs your appetite. Go for a walk, pick up a skipping rope and do three minutes of skipping, or get a weighted hula hoop and do three minutes of that: two really fun and easy ways to exercise without leaving your house.

TROUBLESHOOTING

Some questions that may arise for you about 'how' to eat:

Q. WHAT IF I CAN'T TELL IF I'M ACTUALLY FULL?

You have a mechanism that is located in your solar plexus, just below your ribcage and in the centre of your body. This is a muscle that is designed to control the flow of food to the stomach. For most of us, however, it isn't very strong. As you get familiar using the hunger scale and as you exercise a stronger sense of body awareness, you will begin to be able to feel this muscle close off once you have had enough to eat. Listen to your body and tune in to this muscle. The more attuned you are to it, the more powerful the signal of fullness will become. And remember, if you suspect that you might be full, push the plate away! You can always go back for more as soon as you start to feel hungry again.

Q. IT FEELS SO LIBERATING EATING WHEN I AM ACTUALLY HUNGRY, BUT I STILL FEEL A BIT UNCOMFORTABLE WITH THE IDEA OF EATING WHATEVER I WANT. I STILL FEEL THE ENTRENCHED NEED TO BE 'GOOD', LIKE I DID WHEN I WAS IN 'DIET MODE'. CAN I EAT WHEN I'M HUNGRY BUT STILL EAT WHAT I CONSIDER TO BE 'GOOD' FOODS?

Absolutely not! Diets don't work and you know this by now, so it is essential that you stop eating what you think you should and instead move towards eating what you want. Every time you eat something you don't really want, you are simply reinforcing the idea that you don't know what's best for your body. This is all about building awareness and tuning in to what your body needs and how much of it your body needs. So throw away the idea of trying to be good; there is no space for this notion with Artful Eating!

Q. I AM STILL STRUGGLING TO LEAVE FOOD ON MY PLATE OR NOT FINISH A WHOLE PORTION OF SOMETHING. HAVE YOU ANY OTHER SUGGESTIONS TO HELP ME WITH THIS?

If this is still an issue then you are probably still relying on willpower to limit what you're eating, but that's not the right approach. I want you to shift to using your imagination as opposed to willpower. If you do this, you will find it practically effortless to leave food on your plate as opposed to struggling not to eat a whole portion of something. In the beginning, it will take a bit of effort to associate pleasure with leaving food behind, but what you are doing is reconditioning your mind not to finish a portion. This is the key to feeling freedom with food! As you push the portion away, visualise loving your body and achieving your goal. This is a very empowering action. Raise your spirits into a state of positivity and energy as you consciously push the food away and purposely and consciously feel fantastic as you do it, all the while thinking about how good it will feel when you achieve your goal.

One more good tip I suggest, though, is to break off or separate half the portion before you even start eating and feel the good feelings about doing that! If you're going to have an apple, cut it in half and put the other half back in the fridge: you can always go back for more if you still feel hungry.

SOME QUESTIONS THAT MAY ARISE FOR YOU ABOUT OVERCOMING EMOTIONAL EATING

Q. I FIND THAT I'M ACTUALLY HUNGRY ALL THE TIME. COULD THIS BE AN EMOTIONAL ISSUE AS OPPOSED TO A PHYSICAL ONE?

This is most probably an emotional issue and part of your personal story, which we looked at back in Chapter 6. Go back and revisit your personal story. Try to discern what the underlying cause of the empty feeling you are trying to fill with food is. Reach for an ABC sheet, mark the Activating Trigger as hunger and work through the sheet from there. By doing this exercise you are giving yourself the opportunity to get to the root of the cause of the issue, as opposed to focusing on the symptom: the hunger.

Q. EVERY NOW AND THEN I FALL BACK INTO OLD HABITS AND FEEL GUILTY: WHAT CAN I DO TO GET BACK ON TRACK?

This is a process and it really takes time to move away from old habits and foster new, healthy ones. When you find yourself experiencing a craving or an impulse to binge or eat something when you're not actually hungry, do an ABC sheet. Alternatively, give in to the craving and have the thing you desire, but use the principles

outlined in Chapter 6 and allow yourself half of it. Savour it, enjoy it, chew each mouthful and allow the good feeling of 'treating yourself' to come to the fore, as opposed to feeling guilty and gobbling down the food without registering it. It is when we mindlessly gobble down food without taking the time to enjoy it that we are in danger of overeating.

Q. I REALLY ENJOY ALCOHOL AND I DRINK A LOT: CAN I STILL LOSE WEIGHT?

Let's be clear here, an overconsumption of alcohol is not the reason you are unhappy with your body. After all, there are plenty of thin alcoholics. The real issue with excessive drinking isn't weight gain; it's the effects excessive alcohol consumption has on our bodies and our minds. Drink is often treated as a message to relax and unwind. It can also be used as a way to avoid what is going on in our lives, often at an unconscious level. All the work, internal and external, that you have done throughout the book is designed to help you address these underlying issues and foster new helpful and positive habits and behaviours. By doing this, you will find that you need to drink less and you easily substitute alcohol with other enjoyable and nourishing activities that serve you better.

Q. I WAS DOING REALLY WELL WITH THE PROCESS, APPLYING ALL THE PRINCIPLES AND FEELING REALLY PROUD OF THE CHANGES I HAVE MADE, BUT THEN I BINGED OVER THE WEEKEND AND I FEEL LIKE I'VE FALLEN OFF THE WAGON, AND I'M SO DISAPPOINTED WITH MYSELF. WHAT CAN I DO?

Life often gets in the way: a friend comes to visit, or there is a birthday party, or you've had a particularly stressful week. There will always be things that are beyond your control. The key is to feel good and apply the strategies and tools taught throughout this book to the best of your abilities, most of the time. Remember the phrase 'good enough'. I want you to make a concerted effort to be 'good enough' – not 'good' or 'bad'; just aim for 'good enough' *most of the time*. This is an optimal and, more importantly, sustainable state of mind to be in. You will slip up; you will fall into old, unhelpful patterns of behaviour. The key is what you do next. Instead of beating yourself up and feeling like a failure, focus on all the positive changes you have made and all the fantastic shifts that have occurred for you. Recognise that it is completely human not to be perfect all the time. Forgive yourself and move on. You have all the knowledge, skills and tools now to recognise what has happened and, more importantly, why. Be aware of what happened, be conscious of it and move on.

Q. I HAVE BEEN LOSING WEIGHT ON THE PROGRAMME, BUT NOW IT HAS PLATEAUED. WHAT CAN I DO?

Ask yourself:

- *Are you eating whenever you are actually hungry?*

- *Are you eating things you want to eat as opposed to eating the things you think you should be eating?*

Are you using the steps outlined in Chapter 7: eating slowly and consciously and enjoying each mouthful?

Are you using the hunger scale and stopping when you feel full?

Are you starting from the position of only eating half a portion, and are you pushing the plate away even if there is still food on it, knowing you can always go back for more whenever you feel hungry again?

Reflect on these questions, and if you can honestly answer yes to all of them, then I suggest you slow down even more while you are eating. It is possible that you are not giving your stomach enough time to send a message to the brain to say that it is full. So really take your time, every time you eat something.

Our stomach expands and contracts according to how much food we put in it. In the past, you ate so fast that you were unable to hear the message from your stomach to communicate that you had eaten enough. The result was that your stomach expanded, thereby creating a need for more food to make you feel full.

As you really began to slow down your eating speed, you finally became conscious of what you were eating as you were eating it and there was time for the body and mind to register that you were full. However, our bodies are highly adaptive, so by now you may have become so used to eating at the new slower speed that you have once again stopped listening to your body and so have ended up perhaps eating more than you actually need to. That is why I encourage you to really slow down your eating even more.

Remember when you did the 48-hour Kick-starter? Part of the reason I asked you to do that was so that you could recognise just how much (or indeed little) your body actually needs to be sustained. By slowing down even more as you eat, you will once again find that you are more aware of how much you are eating and how much you actually need to fuel yourself so that you can refine your awareness and tune into your body's satiation signals. By doing this one simple thing, you will notice the body respond as you reignite the realignment process and move towards your goal.

One final suggestion: if you are not happy with the rate of weight loss you are experiencing, make it a rule not to eat after 7 p.m. except on weekends or when you are eating out. This will easily reduce the amount you eat, and you will find that by making this a rule and using the strategy of 'I don't' that it's easy to stick to while you are in the process of realignment. Don't be a slave to this rule and don't skip a meal, but if you manage to eat what you need before the 7 p.m. mark you will certainly notice a difference in your weight loss.

RECIPES

'There is no sincerer love than a love of food.' George Bernard Shaw

In this chapter you will:
discover the basic kitchen essentials that will make cooking easy
discover the store cupboard and fresh ingredients you need to master cooking from scratch,
including when to go organic and when it's okay not to
learn how to enjoy cooking from scratch
learn how to revamp leftovers and the importance of batch cooking.

I want to instil a sense of just how enjoyable it is to cook from scratch and eat extremely well without spending a fortune or slaving over the stove. The concept of this chapter is a week of eating artfully, so you will see how you can revamp leftovers, batch cook for the week and create quick, easy meals that are delicious.

I am a competent home cook and enjoy making food for my family and friends. There are some truly inspirational blogs and cookbooks available to inspire and tantalise, and I am not

even attempting to measure up. What I want to show you is that you can easily make nutritious, quick and delicious food from scratch without needing numerous ingredients. Everything here can be easily adapted, depending on your tastes and what you have to hand. The basic cooking techniques in Chapter 11 should provide you with the foundations for any delicious meal.

In my opinion, simple beats fussy every time, so I favour a plate of roasted red peppers with a spoonful of hummus, some leafy greens, fried halloumi cheese, a sprinkle of seeds and a side of my kitchen-sink brown bread: delicious. This is the kind of food I eat on a daily basis. It takes minutes to prepare, is full of goodness and tastes delicious. There are any number of variations on this: add a poached or boiled egg, swap the halloumi for feta, use a different dressing, instead of hummus have some smashed-up avocado, instead of roast red peppers have roasted butternut squash, or a fillet of fried fish with a drizzle of lemon and olive oil . . . Are you beginning to get a sense of what I mean? Instead of picking a recipe, sourcing all the ingredients and then taking the time to carefully follow the instructions, think about what you fancy, see what you have to hand, and let the ingredients do the work. If you stick to my rule of sourcing the best-quality ingredients, anything you put together will taste fantastic!

BASIC STORE-CUPBOARD INGREDIENTS

PANTRY INGREDIENTS

You should always have these in your pantry. Try to source organic wherever possible.

all-purpose flour
anchovies
apple-cider vinegar
baking powder
balsamic vinegar
black-eyed peas
bouillon
brown rice

brown sugar
caster sugar
coconut oil
corn starch
couscous
Dijon mustard
dried pasta
English mustard
extra virgin olive oil
icing sugar
maple syrup
mixed seeds (raw, unflavoured and not roasted)
nuts: almonds, hazelnuts, pecans, walnuts (raw,

unflavoured and not roasted)
olive oil
porridge oats
raw honey
red and green lentils
red-wine vinegar
rice
sesame oil
soy sauce
Tabasco sauce
tahini (sesame paste)
tinned chickpeas
tinned coconut milk
tinned or dried cannellini beans
tinned or dried kidney beans
tinned tomatoes
tomato purée
unsweetened cocoa powder
white-wine vinegar
wholegrain mustard
wholewheat flour
Worcestershire sauce

HERBS AND SPICES

FRESH HERBS:
basil
coriander
chives
parsley
rosemary
sage
thyme

DRIED HERBS:
basil
coriander
oregano
parsley
rosemary
sage
thyme

SPICES:
black peppercorns
cayenne pepper
chilli powder
cumin seeds
curry powder
five-spice powder
ground cinnamon
ground cumin
ground ginger
ground nutmeg
sea salt flakes
smoked paprika
turmeric
vanilla essence
vanilla pods

Stock up on these store-cupboard ingredients once every two months to make sure you always have the basics to hand.

YOUR WEEKLY SHOP

Your weekly shop should include a mix of the following, depending what's in season, what you plan to cook that week and what you're in the mood for:

apples
artichokes
asparagus
aubergines
avocados
bananas
bean sprouts
beetroot
bell peppers (red, yellow, green)
berries (strawberries, blackberries, blueberries)
broccoli
butter (grass-fed natural butter)
butternut squash
cabbages
cauliflowers
celery
courgettes
cucumbers
eggs (free range)
fennel
garlic
ginger root
green beans
jalapeño peppers
kale
milk and buttermilk
mushrooms
natural yogurt (I love Greek)
onions
oranges
peas
rocket leaves
shallots
spinach
tomatoes

Basic kitchen tools

Here's my list of basic kitchen tools, followed by things that you can pick up over time.

large non-stick frying pan
set of thick-bottomed saucepans
two sheet pans
set of mixing bowls
knives (chef's knife, serrated carving knife, small paring knife)
can opener
speed peeler
mortar and pestle
scales
measuring cups
large colander
large measuring jug
box grater
large grill pan
large casserole pan
wok
metal tongs
wooden spoons
metal whisk
potato masher
ladle
slotted spoon
slotted turner
plastic spatula
rolling pin
sieve
salad spinner
wooden and plastic chopping boards
food processor
hand blender

When to go organic and when it's okay not to

In 2013, the U.S. Department of Agriculture (USDA) tested 3,015 foods and found that almost two-thirds contained pesticide residues. [1] The Environmental Working Group (EWG), a non-profit, non-partisan advocacy group for human health and the environment, calculated that USDA tests found a total of 165 different pesticides on thousands of fruit and vegetables in the 2013 sampling. While these findings might increase your desire to always choose organic over conventionally grown produce, in fact there are many traditionally grown fruits and vegetables that are fine to include in a pesticide-free diet.

The clean 18

asparagus
aubergine
avocado
cabbage
cantaloupe
carrots
cauliflower
grapefruit
kiwi
mango
mushrooms
onion
papaya
peas
pineapple
sweet potato
sweetcorn
watermelon

Okay, so now you know what's safe to eat, below is a list of foods that I encourage you to always ensure are organic because they are the most contaminated fruits and vegetables, sprayed with numerous pesticides:

apples
blueberries
celery
cherry tomatoes
chocolate
coffee
courgettes
cucumbers
grapes
kale
lettuce
peaches
peppers
potatoes
spinach
strawberries

Bring an organic and non-organic list with you when shopping: this will save you money and you can feel confident in the knowledge that you're avoiding unnecessary pesticides. I truly believe you can taste the difference between non-organic and organic produce, and when something is really flavoursome we tend to need less of it to feel satiated.

BATCH COOKING

*Sunday is the day I like to carve out two hours and do my batch cooking for the week.
I'm an early riser, so I like to do it in the morning, before the day runs away, but
you should choose a time and day that suits you. I have my weekly organic fruit and
vegetables delivered on a Saturday, so I have everything I need for the week.*

 # FOUR-BEAN
CHILLI

(PREP TIME 10 MINUTES, COOK TIME 60+ MINUTES, APPROX. 8 SERVINGS)

2 large onions

2 large carrots

2 celery sticks

2 red peppers

2 tbsp olive oil

6 garlic cloves, crushed

3 red chillies, chopped

2 tsp cayenne pepper

4 heaped tsp paprika

800 g of beans of your choice.
I use a mixture of dried mung

beans, adzuki beans, black turtle
beans, black-eye beans and soak
them overnight before using
(you can use the same amount of
steak mince if you prefer)

800 g tin chopped tomatoes

600 ml chicken, beef or vegetable
stock

200 g tin cooked kidney beans,
drained

sea salt flakes and freshly ground
black pepper

As this is a dish I'm batch cooking, I make a lot of it! You will need a big pot, but if you don't want to make that much, just halve the amounts. I like to start with this as it takes the longest to cook, so I can be getting on with the rest while this is simmering away. If you have a slow cooker, even better. This freezes well, it's a cinch to make, and even devoted carnivores struggle to feel disappointed by the lack of meat in this traditionally meaty dish.

Chop the vegetables into small pieces. Don't worry about doing a neat job.

In a large pan, cook the vegetables in olive oil over a medium heat for about 15 minutes without browning.

Add the garlic, chillies, cayenne pepper, paprika and cook for 5 minutes over a medium heat, stirring. Season well.

Add the vegetables, beans, tomatoes and stock to a large pot and bring up to a simmer. (If you have a slow cooker, use this and leave it on high for a couple of hours, stirring occasionally.)

Turn the heat down and cook for another 40 minutes, stirring occasionally.

After 40 minutes, add the kidney beans. Leave on a low heat for another 10 minutes for the kidney beans to heat through.

I always serve this with little bowls of sour cream, grated cheese, jalapeños and chopped raw spring onions. People can add whatever toppings they like, and the colours and flavours are beautiful. This is a really good party dish, as you can cook it in advance. It's also one that tastes even better on day two, as the flavours have had time to marinade. I like to serve it with a glass of red wine or a dark rum and ginger ale with a slice of lime over ice.

BATCH COOKING

VERY VERSATILE
VEGETABLE SOUP

(PREP TIME 10 MINUTES, COOK TIME 20 MINUTES, APPROX. 10 SERVINGS)

1 onion

2 garlic cloves, crushed

6 cups of vegetable or chicken
stock/broth (water will do)

1 tbsp tomato puree/paste

2 400g tins of tomatoes

Then any combination of
the vegetables below (or any
combination of vegetables you
have available):

half a cabbage

4 carrots

2 courgettes

1 red or yellow pepper

½ tsp dried basil or a handful of
fresh basil

½ tsp dried oregano or a handful
of fresh oregano

a good dash of cayenne pepper

sea salt flakes and freshly ground
black pepper

This is the soup my mother made for me daily when I returned home from London after piling on the weight. I still eat this soup at least twice a week, as do my parents. My whole family loves it and it's a cinch to make, as you just use what you have. As long as you have a tin of tomatoes you're off to a good start!

Fry the onions and garlic for 5 minutes in olive oil. (If using carrots, add at this point also.)

Add the broth, tomato paste, tins of tomatoes and all the other ingredients except the courgette.

Simmer until all the vegetables are tender (5–10 minutes). If you're using courgette, add it last, as it only takes 5 minutes to cook. Et voilà! You can leave this as is or blend it – it's up to you.

Mix it up by dolloping on some sour cream, fried bacon bits, chorizo chunks, seeds, fresh herbs or cheese. Little additions make the soup more of a delicious meal than something practical and boring.

Freeze in individual portions in freezer bags so it's ready for lunch or tea. (A note on freezer bags: buy good quality and reuse them – it's more economical and kinder to the environment.)

I always have this soup in my freezer. I absolutely love it and I reach for it after a weekend of indulgence!

BATCH COOKING

COURGETTE CAKE

(PREP TIME 5 MINUTES, COOKING TIME 50 MINUTES, APPROX. 8 SERVINGS)

200 g soft brown sugar

125 ml sunflower oil

3 large eggs, lightly beaten

1 tsp vanilla extract

350 g courgettes, unpeeled

grated zest 1 orange (optional)

300 g self-raising flour

1 tsp baking powder

1 tbsp ground cinnamon

a pinch of salt

I've always got to add something sweet to the mix, so that I have something available if I have guests or fancy something to go with my mid-morning coffee, which I affectionately refer to as elevenses. It is the easiest cake you'll ever make, as the courgette melts into the batter, making it lovely and moist. It will keep for a couple of days and freezes well. I especially love this cake as it doesn't require any accoutrements: no need for cream, icing or butter; it tastes delicious all on its own! I like to slice half the cake, as the remainder will be eaten within the week. Wrap the individual slices in parchment and freeze them, ready to pop in the toaster whenever you're in the mood for something sweet.

Pre-heat oven to 160°C if you have a fan-assisted oven, 180°C otherwise, or Gas 4.

Grease and line a 1 kg loaf tin with baking parchment.

Grate the courgette and squeeze out as much liquid as you can, so the cake isn't too soggy.

In a mixing bowl, beat together the sugar, oil, eggs and vanilla until light in colour and a bit fluffy. Then stir in the grated courgette and orange zest.

Fold the flour, baking powder, cinnamon and salt into the wet mixture.

Pour mixture into the loaf tin.
Bake for 50 minutes, or until a skewer comes out clean when inserted into the middle of the cake.

Remove from the oven and allow to cool a little, then turn out.

Store covered in the fridge (remember there are no preservatives!) for up to 5 days.

BATCH COOKING

GORGEOUS GREEN SMOOTHIE

(PREP TIME 15 MINUTES. 7 FREEZABLE SERVINGS)

---

a generous handful of spinach and/or kale

a few leaves of lettuce

¼ apple

1 celery stick

juice of ½ a lemon

a handful of fresh mint

½ slice of pineapple

¼ cucumber

a few cubes of ice (for thickening)

optional extras: coriander or parsley, and a few almonds, brazil nuts or seeds (if you have a good blender)

I am not a big fan of fruit smoothies on a regular basis. They are an excellent treat, but I don't recommend them as a daily indulgence. Eating fruit in its natural form is much more filling. Think about it: you could easily eat an apple, banana, some berries and an orange, swallowed down with some natural yogurt, and that's a lot of fruit in one sitting! However, there is one smoothie I swear by. If I have it in the morning I know I am set up for the day, having had a big dose of vitamins and minerals first thing. Freeze individual portions in freezer bags, so they are ready to whizz up in the morning: this saves so much time and, to be honest, I'd struggle to have one each morning if I had to wash and prepare all the ingredients on a daily basis.

Combine ingredients in a blender and puree until smooth, about 1 minute, adding water to reach the desired consistency.

SUNDAY

BREAKFAST

Once I've finished batch cooking, I turn to breakfast. As it's Sunday, I'll take the dogs for a short walk to the local delicatessen, where they make beautiful fresh pastries and breads. I have to get there early on a Sunday, otherwise there is nothing left! I like a pain au chocolat with a coffee, and the Sunday papers. Heaven!

LUNCH

 # ROAST CHICKEN

(PREP TIME 10 MINUTES, COOKING TIME 80 MINUTES,
APPROX. 6 SERVINGS)

2 medium onions

4 carrots

4 sticks celery

1 bulb garlic

whole free-range chicken
(approx. 3.5 lb)

olive oil or coconut oil

sea salt and freshly ground black
pepper

1 small bunch fresh thyme,
rosemary, bay or sage, or a
mixture

optional extras: honey or lemon
juice

I love to roast a free-range chicken on a Sunday: we enjoy it, and then we have some variation of the leftovers in a curry or a chicken salad, and I make chicken broth from the bones. The best part? It really is the easiest thing to make. I pop it in the oven, then walk my dogs along the beach, and when I come back the smells are amazing and I've worked up an appetite!

Preheat your oven to 240°C/ 220°C fan/gas 9.

There's no need to peel the vegetables, just wash and roughly chop them into large bite-sized chunks.

Put the vegetables and garlic into a large roasting tray and drizzle with olive oil.

Drizzle the chicken with olive oil or coconut oil and season well with sea salt flakes and freshly ground black pepper, rubbing it all over.

Place the fresh herbs inside the chicken and around the vegetables also.

If you are using honey or lemon juice, rub it on the chicken now. Turn the heat down to 200°C/180° fan/gas 6 and place the chicken on top of the vegetables in the roasting tray and put it into the oven.

Cook the chicken for 1 hour and 20 minutes, or until the juices run clear. The vegetables will be full of juicy flavour.

Use the juices of the chicken and a little bit of the roasted vegetables left in the roasting tin to make the gravy: whizz it up, add a splash of hot water or a dash of red wine if necessary, et voilà.

Serve with some lightly fried green beans, new potatoes boiled with some fresh mint, and the leftover red wine.

Once we have eaten our fill, I take whatever chicken is left off the carcass and store it for later in the week. With the leftover carcass I'll make stock, or its in-vogue nomenclature 'bone broth'!

SUNDAY

 STOCK

(PREP TIME 2 MINUTES, COOK TIME 6–12 HOURS)

---

chicken carcass (beef bones or lamb bones work also)

handful of onions, leeks, carrots or celery

1 tbsp black peppercorns

pinch of sea salt flakes

3 bay leaves

squeeze of lemon or a splash of apple-cider vinegar

Add all the ingredients to a large pot of cold water (the water level should cover the bones by a good amount, though leave some room at the top of the pot).

Cover with a lid and bring to the boil, then reduce the heat and simmer with the lid on for at least 6 hours (12 for beef or lamb). Skim off any foam that rises. The longer you leave the bones to simmer, the more nutrients are released into the stock, so 6 hours is the minimum I recommend. If you have a slow cooker, leave for 12 hours on high.

Once it's ready, strain the liquid using a fine mesh strainer and leave to cool before storing. I like to store the broth in old jam jars in the fridge, where it will keep for about a week, and in reusable freezer bags for the freezer.

SUNDAY

🌿 TEA 🌿

After a lovely roast lunch, I'm just not that hungry, so I'll have something light, simple and quick to make.

  # CAPRESE SALAD

(PREP TIME 5 MINUTES, APPROX. 4 SERVINGS)

---

4 juicy large organic tomatoes

2 buffalo mozzarella balls

a generous handful of fresh basil leaves

a large glug of olive oil

sea salt flakes and freshly ground black pepper

This is a classic and it is truly delicious. It is essential when making this salad that you use really good-quality ingredients. This will elevate the flavour and pleasure immensely!

Slice or chop the tomatoes.

Tear up the mozzarella.

Sprinkle with fresh basil leaves, a drizzle of olive oil and some sea salt flakes and freshly ground black pepper, et voilà!

Serve with some crunchy fresh baguette.

MONDAY

It's the beginning of the week and I have a glut of leftovers that I will certainly make good use of. But I'll start with a hearty breakfast. You've no doubt heard it said many, many times, and this is because it's true: breakfast is the most important meal of the day. Yet too often we rush or even skip it. I like to take my time and enjoy breakfast, as it marks the beginning of the day. Start the day as you mean for it to continue: nourishing yourself, contemplating how you'd like the day to go over a dish of something delicious.

❧ BREAKFAST ❧

I start every day with a cup of warm water and the juice of half a lemon, followed by a glass of my gorgeous green smoothie, which is my absolute favourite morning booster. A glass every morning and I know I'm set up for the day!

NUTTY NATURAL YOGURT

3 tbsp natural Greek yogurt

1 tbsp porridge oats

5 pecans smashed in a pestle and mortar (or any nuts you fancy)

1 tsp honey

optional extra: squeeze of lemon juice to taste

This is one of my favourite breakfasts. Play around with this recipe to get the consistency you like. The natural yogurt must be of good quality and, ideally, Greek-style. I recommend you try getting one locally made and not mass-produced as it will have good bacteria, which your gut needs.

Mix all the ingredients together and enjoy. Find the balance of flavours and consistency that you like.

MID-MORNING SNACK, OR WHAT I AFFECTIONATELY CALL 'ELEVENSES'

A cup of coffee and a slice of courgette cake.

MONDAY

🌿 DINNER 🌿

I like to have my dinner in the middle of the day. This may be a boarding-school hangover, but it's also because my clinic hours are usually in the afternoon, right up to the late evening, so I need to have something substantial to keep me going.

Four-bean chilli served with brown rice, sliced spring onions and guacamole.

GUACAMOLE

(PREP TIME 5 MINUTES, APPROX. 5 SERVINGS)

---

3 medium avocados

1 tomato

2 spring onions

a handful of coriander

2 tbsp fresh lemon or lime juice

sea salt flakes and freshly ground black pepper

Avocados are full of potassium, and vitamins K, E, and B. They also have a very high amount of fibre. Guacamole is one of those staples I'll whip up for lunch with crudités.

Finely slice the tomato.

Place all the ingredients in your food processor and whizz it up. Alternatively, you can mash up the avocado and finely chop all the ingredients for a chunkier recipe or, if you're feeling lazy, simply mash up some avocado and let the wonderful flavour speak for itself!

Dollop over chilli.

Elevate a simple salad with a dollop of guacamole and a variety of beans (kidney, chickpeas and cannelloni beans).

It's best to enjoy this straight away, as guacamole goes brown if it comes into contact with the air. If you cover it in clingfilm along with the avocado stone and make sure the clingfilm touches the guacamole, it will last a day.

MONDAY

TEA

GARDEN GREEN SALAD WITH SUNDAY'S CHICKEN

(PREP TIME 5 MINUTES, APPROX. 2 SERVINGS)

green leaves (any type you have): spinach, lettuce, kale, rocket and so on

½ cucumber

2 spring onions

2 tomatoes

optional extras: a handful of seeds or chopped nuts, a couple of chunks of cheese (approx. 50 g per person of feta, fried or grilled halloumi, or any cheese you fancy)

My simple, healthy and tasty take on 'fast food'. Regardless of the health benefits of eating fresh raw vegetables in their natural form, salad is just so simple and really delicious, so it should be an integral part of the fabric of your diet. Anything goes, but I find that if you bring salad to lunch it can get really soggy and not too tasty. So, if you can, assemble it at work.

Chop the cucumber, spring onions and tomatoes.

Mix the ingredients and, just before serving, drizzle with a

home-made salad dressing.

For dinner, serve with a piece of fried or grilled chicken or fish seasoned lightly with a squeeze of lemon juice, sea salt flakes and freshly ground black pepper.

Try frying up some chorizo chunks or bacon lardons.

Add some roasted red peppers and hummus.

I'll follow this with a piece of fruit, not necessarily a whole apple or orange, but a taste of whatever I have, sliced and laid out on a plate, perhaps with a few thin slices of cheese.

TUESDAY

❧ BREAKFAST ❧

A cup of hot water with lemon, with a dash of turmeric and some grated ginger.

A glass of gorgeous green smoothie.

AVOCADO TOAST

(PREP TIME 5 MINUTES, APPROX. 2 SERVINGS)

1 avocado

squeeze of lemon juice

sea salt flakes

2 slices kitchen-sink brown bread

2 poached eggs

optional extra: garnish with some chilli flakes and a drizzle of olive oil

This dish sums up everything I advocate about home cooking: it's simple, delicious, quick to make, has few ingredients, you can jazz it up with whatever takes your fancy so there are limitless variations, it's filling, so good for you, it's colourful, it works for breakfast, brunch, lunch or tea, it's gorgeous to look at, and any guest would be delighted to eat it.

Cut the avocado in half, remove the pit and scoop the flesh into a bowl.

Add the lemon juice and sea salt, to taste (or not, the avocado is indeed perfect on its own).

Mash the ingredients together with a fork, keeping the texture chunky.

Spread half the mash onto each piece of toasted kitchen-sink brown bread.

Top with a poached egg.

ELEVENSES

A cup of coffee and some artisan chocolates.

TUESDAY

❧ LUNCH ❧

Lunch can be tricky if you don't plan ahead. For those working in an environment where there are so many tasty options on your doorstep, I encourage you to take the time to make your own lunch. You'll save a fortune! Recent studies have shown that workers fork out more than £2,500 (€2,900) a year for small purchases such as coffees, breakfast, lunch and snacks.[2] That is a lot of money, so preparing your lunch is a really good idea. Also, you know exactly what you're eating. When I was working outside of home, my regular lunch was a 'dinner'-type meal that I would make and freeze on the weekend, like a chilli, or salad with Sunday's roast chicken.

BUTTERNUT SQUASH & RICOTTA

(PREP TIME 10 MINUTES, COOKING TIME 40–50 MINUTES,
APPROX. 2 SERVINGS)

2 small butternut squash (I'll use the second one to make a soup tomorrow)

1–2 garlic cloves (unpeeled), lightly bashed

a few sprigs of thyme

2 tbsp extra virgin olive or

rapeseed oil, plus extra to serve

sea salt flakes and freshly ground black pepper

100 g ricotta (feta works well too)

30–40 g thinly sliced Parma ham or lightly fried bacon lardons

a squeeze of lemon juice

Butternut squash is such a versatile vegetable. I love to roast it and use it as a base for soups, salads and this simple hearty dish.

Preheat the oven to 190°C /170°C fan/gas 5. Peel and deseed the squash, then cut into chunks.

Put into a roasting dish with the garlic and a few thyme sprigs, if using.

Trickle over 2 tablespoons of extra virgin olive oil, season with sea salt flakes and freshly ground black pepper and toss well.

Roast for 40 to 50 minutes, or until the squash is tender and starting to caramelise, giving it a stir halfway through cooking.

Discard the garlic and thyme and leave to cool completely.

Put half the roasted squash aside to make soup later in the week, then place the remainder on individual plates or a large platter. Dot the ricotta over the top.

Tear the ham into shreds and scatter over the squash and ricotta. Tear the leaves from the rest of the thyme sprigs, if you have them, and scatter over the dish.

Season with sea salt flakes, freshly ground black pepper and extra virgin olive oil. Finish with a squeeze of lemon juice, then serve.

Follow this with a handful of grapes for dessert.

TUESDAY

 TEA

Very versatile vegetable soup.

KITCHEN-SINK BROWN BREAD

(PREP TIME 5 MINUTES, COOKING TIME 40 MINUTES)

---

300 g wholewheat flour (if you prefer, you can use a mix of plain and wholewheat)

100 g ground flaxseed or linseed

100 g oats

70 g seeds of your choosing (I use a combination of sunflower, chia, pine nuts and linseeds)

1 tbsp of baking soda or powder

sea salt flakes

500 ml buttermilk

1 tbsp of honey or maple syrup

This is a pantry staple, as it's great for breakfast, but it also makes a delicious foundation for any type of lunch you fancy: poached egg and avocado, garlic and tomatoes, wild smoked salmon and butter with a squeeze of lemon. Let your imagination run wild! What's also great about this bread is that I fill it with nuts, seeds, ground linseeds

and oats, so it's full of goodness.

Preheat the oven to 200°C/180°C fan/gas 6.

Mix together the dry ingredients with a spoon.

Slowly add the buttermilk, mixing as you go. Depending on the types of seeds you use, you will need less or more milk. The key is to bind the ingredients so that they hold together in a sticky wett-ish lump.

Dust flour on a baking tray and put the mixture in the middle of the tray, or use a lightly greased loaf tin.

Let it cook for approximately 40 minutes, depending on your oven. You'll know it's ready when you stick a knife in it and the knife comes out clean, and when you knock on the base it sounds hollow.

Leave to cool on a wire rack for 10 to 15 minutes.

WEDNESDAY

🌿 BREAKFAST 🌿

A cup of warm water and lemon, a glass of my gorgeous green smoothie and nutty natural yogurt.

🌿 ELEVENSES 🌿

 # MINI SCONES

(PREP TIME 5 MINUTES, COOKING TIME 10 MINUTES,
APPROX. 10 MINI SCONES)

---

225 g self-raising flour (you can substitute white flour for wholegrain flour or brown flour)

pinch of sea salt flakes

25 g caster sugar (if you wish to make savoury scones replace the sugar with the same amount of flour)

25 g butter, softened

150 ml milk

optional extra: raisins

These scones can be whipped up in 15 minutes and I often make them if someone pops in unexpectedly. By the time my visitor has settled down and the tea is brewed, the scones are ready to enjoy. Try with some clotted cream and jam – delicious!

Preheat the oven to 220°C/ 200°C/gas mark 8.

Mix together the flour, salt and sugar in a bowl. (If using raisins, add at this point.)

Rub in the soft butter.

Add sufficient milk to make a dough.

Turn onto a floured board and gently knead to remove any cracks.

Roll out roughly to about one-inch thickness and cut out scones in small circles.

Bake in oven for approximately 10 minutes.

Cool on a wire tray.

Serve with a dollop of cream and strawberry jam!

WEDNESDAY

LUNCH

BUTTERNUT SQUASH SOUP

(PREP TIME 15 MINUTES, COOKING TIME, EXCLUDING ROASTING THE
SQUASH, 40 MINUTES, APPROX. 6 SERVINGS)

---

1 red onion

1 carrot

2 cloves garlic

1 tbsp olive oil

2 sprigs fresh rosemary

½ fresh red chilli

sea salt flakes and freshly ground
black pepper

1 butternut squash

2 litres of chicken stock

optional extra: 1 celery stick

Use yesterday's leftover butternut squash, or chop a butternut squash in half and roast for 30 minutes at 180°C/160°C fan/gas 4.

Peel and chop the onion, carrot and garlic. (Trim and chop the celery stick, if using.) Remove leaves from the rosemary sprigs.

Deseed and finely chop the red chilli.

Put a large saucepan on a medium heat and pour in a generous tablespoon of olive oil.

Add the onion, carrot, garlic, celery (if using), rosemary leaves,

chilli and a good pinch of sea salt flakes and freshly ground black pepper. Cook gently for about 10 minutes on a medium heat.

Add the squash and the stock to the pan, bring to the boil and simmer for around 10 more minutes.

Whizz the soup with a hand blender or pour it into a liquidiser and pulse until you have a smooth purée.

Sprinkle on some feta or Parmesan cheese, or some crispy fried bacon lardons, small fried chunks of chorizo or some lightly toasted seeds.

Follow this with a home-made tea infusion (I like mint) and a small slice of watermelon.

WEDNESDAY

TEA

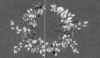 GREEK SALAD

(PREP TIME 10 MINUTES, APPROX. 4 SERVINGS)

---

4 large tomatoes

½ cucumber (leave the skin on)

2 small or 1 large red onion

200 g feta cheese

1 green pepper

dried oregano (fresh is even better)

good-quality extra virgin olive oil

sea salt flakes

optional extras: a squeeze of lemon and Kalamata (black) olives

---

This is my all-time favourite salad and one I eat regularly. Make sure the tomatoes are really ripe and juicy: this is key! Also, the cucumber should be chilled and from the fridge. This salad must be served cold to be truly refreshing.

Roughly slice the tomatoes Roughly chop the cucumber, and peel and thinly slice the red onion. Cut the feta into thick slices, or go authentic and leave it as one big slab on top of the salad.

Thinly slice the green pepper.

Most people use dried oregano, but it is much better with fresh: scatter either on the salad.

Add a glug of good-quality extra virgin olive oil.

Sprinkle with some sea salt flakes. If using, add some Kalamata olives and a squeeze of lemon juice.

Serve with some grilled tuna fillets and a squeeze of lemon or just enjoy with some crunchy fresh French baguette.

Follow this with a herbal tea and an artisan chocolate.

THURSDAY

🌿 BREAKFAST 🌿

A cup of warm water and lemon, a glass of my gorgeous green smoothie, and a boiled egg with some kitchen-sink brown bread with butter, strawberry jam and topped with a slice of Gruyère cheese.

🌿 ELEVENSES 🌿

Coffee and courgette cake.

🌿 DINNER 🌿

Reheat a bowl of four-bean chilli with a gorgeous green salad topped with home-made salad dressing.

Home-made dressings make a huge difference to any salad and are that simple extra touch that creates a delicious meal from a few simple ingredients. Have some fun with making them and trying different flavours. The great thing about a fabulous dressing is that you can stay very simple with the food you're dressing. Try steaming some asparagus and adding a dressing, et voilà: a simple, flavoursome lunch or tea in minutes.

Make more dressing than you need. You can keep it in the fridge in a jar for ages: vinaigrettes last about 2 weeks and dressings with fresh ingredients, like chopped shallots, will last at least a week.

Do not feel the need to dress the salad straightaway. Once a salad is dressed it won't keep and really the whole thing needs to be eaten. So if I've made up a big salad, I'll leave the dressing in the jar and let people dress their own serving.

CLASSIC LEMON & OLIVE OIL DRESSING

1 tbsp lemon juice

3 tbsp olive oil

sea salt flakes and freshly ground black pepper

This is a very useful dressing which goes well with greens.

Whisk together the ingredients, taste, and adjust seasoning.

FRENCH DRESSING

40 g Dijon mustard

80 ml white-wine vinegar

350 ml rapeseed oil or olive oil

sea salt flakes and freshly ground black pepper

A French classic, delicious over lightly steamed asparagus or green beans. Also perfect with any green salad.

Mix the mustard and vinegar together in a blender. While still running, slowly add the oil until you have a fully emulsified dressing. Season with sea salt flakes and freshly ground black pepper.

THURSDAY

HONEY & MUSTARD DRESSING

1 garlic clove, crushed

sea salt flakes and freshly ground black pepper

2 tsp Dijon mustard

2 tsp runny honey

3 tbsp white-wine vinegar

100 ml sunflower oil

This is just glorious poured over sliced avocado and some roasted free-range chicken fillets.

Simply whisk all the ingredients together and season.

RED ONION & SHALLOT

1 small red onion or shallot, finely chopped

1 tbsp balsamic vinegar

2 tsp soft brown sugar

2 tbsp olive oil

sea salt flakes and freshly ground black pepper

Use this with roasted beetroot and lentils topped with goat's cheese or feta.

Combine the onion or shallot, vinegar and sugar, then season. Then add the olive oil and stir well.

BASIL DRESSING

a bunch of basil leaves
(remove stems)

1 garlic clove, crushed

100 ml olive oil

sea salt flakes and freshly
ground black pepper

Best for drizzling over fresh
tomatoes, grilled courgettes or a
tomato salad, but you can take it
a step further by adding a handful
of pine nuts and Parmesan
for a simple pesto, which is
truly delicious with spirallised
courgette or pasta.

Blend the ingredients together.

THURSDAY

🌿 TEA 🌿

Green salad with hummus and a side of roasted peppers.

 # HUMMUS

(PREP TIME 5 MINUTES, APPROX. 6–8 SERVINGS)

---

800 g drained well-cooked or canned chickpeas, liquid reserved

1 tbsp tahini

3 tbsp extra virgin olive oil, plus oil for drizzling

2 cloves garlic, peeled and crushed

a good pinch of sea salt flakes

and freshly ground black pepper

1 tbsp ground cumin or paprika, plus a sprinkling for garnish

juice of 1 lemon, plus more as needed

optional extra: fresh parsley leaves for garnish

This eons-old Middle Eastern classic is a great go-to if you're not sure what to make, or some guests turn up unexpectedly of an evening. I can make a batch of this at the last minute to use as a dip or a spread. You can make hummus without tahini (sesame paste); it will be a little looser and less complex-tasting, but still incredibly good. If by some miracle you don't eat it all(!), it

should last in the fridge for 3–5 days.

Put everything except the parsley in a food processor and begin to process. Add the chickpea liquid or water as needed to allow the machine to produce a smooth pureé.

Taste and adjust the seasoning and ingredients to taste.

Serve, drizzled with the olive oil and sprinkled with a bit more cumin or paprika and some chopped parsley.

Hummus is very versatile: serve on toast, with crudités, as part of a salad, or with roasted vegetables or just roasted red peppers. Try spreading a light coating of hummus on top of portobello mushrooms and place under the grill for a couple of minutes.

FRIDAY

❧ BREAKFAST ❧

A cup of warm water and lemon, a glass of my gorgeous green smoothie, and nutty natural yogurt.

❧ ELEVENSES ❧

Coffee and a mini scone.

❧ LUNCH ❧

Very versatile vegetable soup.

❧ DINNER ❧

 # BASIC RISOTTO

(PREP TIME 5 MINUTES, COOKING TIME, WHICH WILL REQUIRE ONGOING SUPERVISION, 35 MINUTES – SO POUR A GLASS OF WINE AND PUT ON SOME MUSIC – APPROX. 6 SERVINGS)

2 tbsp olive oil

1 large onion, finely chopped

2 cloves garlic, finely chopped

400 g risotto rice

1 l chicken, fish or vegetable stock as appropriate

a small knob of butter

90 g Parmesan cheese

sea salt flakes and freshly ground black pepper

optional extra: glass of white wine

optional extras: try these variations: ½ head finely chopped celery, 2 tbsp fresh chopped mint and 2 tsp lemon zest; mushrooms, any type, four large handfuls roughly chopped and grilled on a griddle pan or under the grill; a butternut squash, roughly chopped into small chunks and roasted; some leftover cooked chicken or 4 roasted chicken breasts; approximately 4 fillets of fish, whatever type your fishmonger recommends on the day; a large bunch of asparagus, roughly chopped, woody ends discarded; 250 g peas, a handful of mint and the zest and juice of a lemon

Finely chop the onion and garlic. Heat the stock.

In a separate pan, heat the olive oil, add the onion and garlic, and fry on a low heat for about 15 minutes.

When the vegetables have softened, add the rice and turn up the heat. The rice will now begin to lightly fry, so keep stirring it. After a minute, it will look slightly translucent. (If using, add the glass of wine now and keep stirring until it has cooked into the rice.)

Add your first ladle of hot stock and a good pinch of sea salt flakes. Turn down the heat to a simmer. Keep adding ladlefuls of stock, allowing it to be absorbed before adding the next. This will take around 15 minutes. Taste the rice: is it cooked? Carry on adding stock until the rice is soft but with a slight bite.

Don't forget to check the seasoning carefully. If you run out of stock before the rice is cooked, add some boiling water. (If you are adding vegetables, cooked chicken or fish, or another variation, add it at this point and cook for a further 5 minutes.)

Remove from the heat and add the butter and Parmesan. Stir well. Place a lid on the pan and allow to sit for 2 minutes. This is the most important part of making the perfect risotto, as this is when it becomes outrageously creamy, as it should be!

This is a great dish to eat with friends, as you can chat while you stir! Eat it as soon as possible, while the risotto retains its beautiful texture.

SATURDAY

A cup of warm water and lemon, and a glass of my gorgeous green smoothie.

🌿 BRUNCH 🌿

SAVOURY PANCAKES

(PREP TIME 10 MINUTES, COOKING TIME 15 MINUTES, APPROX. 4 SERVINGS)

FOR THE PANCAKES

300 g plain flour (you can substitute the flour for buckwheat, wholegrain or chickpea flour or ground porridge oats, or you could use any combination of 60 g the above with 40 g of ground flaxseed for every 100 g)

pinch of salt

3 free-range eggs

1 tbsp melted butter or sunflower oil

300 ml milk

FOR THE FILLING

olive oil or coconut oil

½ a medium red onion

1 large (any colour) pepper

200 g courgette

100 g cheese (any type)

1 bunch parsley

1 stem of mint

sea salt flakes and freshly ground black pepper (optional)

FOR THE PANCAKES

Pancakes are the culinary equivalent of a blank canvas, as they're very versatile. I love eating them for breakfast, lunch or tea! You can fill them with whatever takes your fancy: use your imagination and the flavours and combinations you enjoy. I also do love the traditional dollop of butter, sugar and lemon, a glorious combination.

Sift the flour and salt into a mixing bowl and make a well in the centre.

Crack the eggs into the well add the melted butter or oil and half the milk.

Beat well to make a smooth batter. Stir in the remaining milk.

Ideally leave to stand for about 30 minutes.

Stir again before using, but if you don't have time or patience you can use immediately.

FOR THE FILLING

Heat a tablespoon of oil in a frying pan and add a few tablespoons of batter for the first pancake. Flip when the edges are dry and bubbles form on the surface. Repeat until all the batter is used, then keep the pancakes warm under foil or in the oven.

Grate the courgette, then press to remove some of the moisture. Finely chop the red onion, parsley and mint. Dice the pepper. Grate the cheese.

For the filling, heat the oil in a frying pan and fry the pepper and onion for 3 minutes, then add the courgettes for a further 1 minute. Remove from the pan and mix with cheese and fresh herbs. Spoon filling onto the hot pancakes, fold and serve.

Follow this with half an apple, or whatever fruit you fancy, and a cup of herbal tea.

SATURDAY

❧ DINNER ❧

 # FRIED SCALLOPS

(PREP TIME 5 MINUTES, COOKING TIME 5 MINUTES, APPROX. 2 SERVINGS)

---

2 tbsp olive oil

1 bunch spring onions

50 g frozen peas

sea salt flakes and freshly ground
black pepper

6 scallops, cleaned, with corals
attached if you like

knob of butter

1 garlic clove

a squeeze of lemon juice

This is my idea of fast food, as it's quick and easy to prepare, and uses just a few simple ingredients. Indeed, it also makes a great starter and tastes great with a glass of wine.

Trim the spring onions and cut at an angle. Peel the garlic clove and finely chop or grate. Clean the scallops, but leave the corals attached if you like.

Put the frozen peas in a sieve and pour a cup of boiling water over them.

Heat a tablespoon of olive oil in a frying pan over a medium-low heat. Add the spring onions and

let them sweat gently for about 5 minutes, until soft. Add the peas and toss for a minute or two. Season with sea salt flakes and freshly ground black pepper, remove from the pan and set aside.

Add another tablespoon of oil and turn the heat up high.

Season the scallops and add when the pan is very hot: they should sizzle when they hit the pan.

Leave them for about 1 minute, then carefully turn one over: if golden-brown, flip all the scallops over and cook until caramelised on the other side.

Reduce the heat to medium-low and return the peas and spring onions to the pan, along with the butter and garlic.

Toss, take off the heat, add a squeeze of lemon, and enjoy with a glass of crisp white wine.

SATURDAY

 DESSERT

ETON MESS

(PREP TIME 5 MINUTES, APPROX. 4 SERVINGS)

---

500 g strawberries

2 tsp caster sugar

500 ml whipping cream (a really good-quality Greek or natural yogurt tastes just as good, I promise!)

4 small meringue nests (from a packet)

4 sprigs mint

This is my go-to easy dinner-party dessert. It takes minutes to make, it looks amazing and it's simply delicious! Try any variety of summer fruits and berries.

Hull and chop the strawberries and sprinkle with sugar.

Whip the cream in a large bowl until thick but still soft.

Roughly crumble in 4 meringue nests. Leave some chunks for texture.

Fold the meringue, cream and fruit mixture together, keeping back a ladleful (100 g) of strawberries.

Arrange in four glasses (small white wine glasses are an ideal portion size) and top each one with some of the remaining strawberries.

Top each with a sprig of mint.

DIGESTIF

ARTFUL EATING
FOR LIFE

'Most folks are just about as happy as we make up our minds to be.' Abraham Lincoln
'Happiness is when what you think, what you say, and what you do are in harmony.'
Mahatma Gandhi

Thank you for taking the time to read this book. I admire you for being courageous and curious enough to embark on a new way of being. You have decided to take action, and you are now enjoying the benefits of the powerful knowledge you have gained. I ask you to take the momentum you have created and run with it. Whether you have read this book in its entirety all in one go, or whether you have taken your time and gone through each chapter step by step, remember that you can always revisit any chapter or action.

The changes and shifts in mindset taught throughout these pages are so simple, but it takes commitment on your part to adopt this way of being and feeling. Committing to experiencing a beautiful healthy body and mind takes effort at the start. When you're learning a new skill, you have to consciously practise in the beginning, until it becomes second nature. So make the conscious effort to implement these teachings: you will experience and enjoy a whole new way of being in the world that will change the course of your life. I know that sounds dramatic, but it's true. Your health is a gift that must be cherished and protected. I wrote this book to share with you my processes, which result in a healthy mind and a healthy body.

I have just one final action I would like you to do: only do this once you have gone through and completed all the actions throughout the book. This final exercise is here to encourage you to think about your future and commit to maintaining this new lifestyle permanently. It is inspired by the wonderful designer and teacher Debbie Millman.[1]

ACTION #1: A FIVE-YEAR PLAN FOR A WONDERFUL LIFE (1 HOUR, BUT PERHAPS A COUPLE OF DAYS' CONTEMPLATION FIRST)

Take some time and space to reflect on your future. How do you want your life to be? How do you want to feel and what do you want to experience? I want you to write a detailed essay in which you imagine what your life could be if you could do anything you wanted without any fear of failure or fear of falling back into old habits. Paint a picture. Let this essay be full of hope, optimism, well-being and goodness.

Imagine it is exactly five years from now. Write an essay describing your day from when you wake up in the morning until you go to bed in the evening.

- *What does a day in your life look like?*
- *What are you doing?*
- *Where are you living?*
- *Who are you living with?*
- *Do you have a partner? What are they like?*
- *Do you have children? What are they like?*
- *What type of house are you living in? Does it have a garden? Do you have pets?*
- *What do you look like and how do you feel?*
- *What kind of clothes do you have? What is your hair like?*
- *Are you fit and healthy?*
- *What is the decor like?*
- *What type of artwork do you have on your walls?*
- *What is your kitchen like?*
- *What are you working on and who are you working with?*
- *What do you want?*
- *What are you reading?*
- *What are you eating?*
- *What excites you?*
- *What do you enjoy doing?*

Write about this one day five years from now. What does your whole day look like? Start from the minute you wake up and brush your teeth, have your breakfast (which should start with a cup of lemon in hot water and a gorgeous green smoothie!), all the way through to when you go to bed at night.

DREAM BIG.

Don't allow practicality of the limitations of what you think is realistic to hinder your dream future. Write it all down in as much detail as possible and trust that you don't have to share it with anyone: it is just for you. Invest in this essay. Invest your energy, hope and love in it. Write this day like your life depends on it, because it does.

Then read it, once a year, and see what happens.

It is a truly magical exercise.

You will be so surprised by taking the time to write out your future, imagining a future where you are happy, healthy and enjoying life and your body is an extremely powerful thing. Anything is possible. By writing out your dream life, this is a love letter to yourself. You are already making a decision about how you choose to experience your life, instead of allowing life to happen to you. To give yourself a dream and declare what you want from your life provides you with purpose, vision and possibility. I'm excited for you to see what your future brings.

Thank you so much for letting me lead you on this Artful Eating journey. I really appreciate you investing your time and committing to this shift in your mindset and your story. It is an honour and a privilege to share this journey with you. You now have all the tools you need to create a healthy, vibrant body inside and out.

Remember to enjoy the process!

FINDING A THERAPIST

There are many modalities within the fields of counselling and psychotherapy, so it can be very difficult to know how to go about finding the right therapist for you. Personal recommendations are always good, so do ask friends, family or your GP. The most important element for engagement in therapy is the therapeutic relationship. You need to feel comfortable and confident in your therapist for the work to have an effect, so I encourage you to shop around. Ring up prospective therapists and ask some questions: how long have they been practising? Where have they trained? What are their qualifications? And finally, what is their orientation? These questions should give you some sense of their abilities and experience. You need to establish if there is a connection, that you have a mutual agreement about the purpose of therapy and that there is a mutual agreement about the methods you will use in pursuit of this purpose. A therapist's job is to help you to sort out your issues in a way that you cannot do by yourself.

As a psychoanalytic psychotherapist, I naturally favour this modality, as the approach helps you to hear and see the things in your actions and behaviour that you are unaware of, but which are determining your position in life. In psychoanalysis we privilege the unconscious, that part of you which has the greatest determination of how you think, act and feel. Successive empirical studies have shown that not only do patients who choose psychoanalysis improve during therapy, but they also continue to improve after therapy has finished.[1] Research also shows that when differently oriented therapists choose therapy for themselves, they often opt to see a psychoanalyst.[2]

A main difference with other forms of therapy is that rather than focus solely on the relief of symptoms, psychoanalysis aims to free the client across a broad range of emotions, current and past. Recent research compares psychoanalysis with other psychological and

pharmacological treatments and demonstrates that, in many cases, it is the most effective treatment for a wide range of problems, including depression, anxiety, panic and stress-related physical ailments. In counter tendency to many non-psychoanalytic treatments, the benefits of therapy were also shown to increase after treatment had ended.[3]

Engaging in therapy is a significant commitment of time and money, but it is an incredibly worthwhile investment in your well-being, your relationships and your future. My clients often tell me that it is the best investment they've ever made! So if you feel you have identified issues that you need help to work through, get in touch with your GP or search online for reputable therapists.

ENDNOTES

Introduction

1. Traci Mann et al., 'Medicare's search for effective obesity treatments: Diets are not the answer', *American Psychologist,* 62/3 (2007), 220–33.

2. Nielsen, *We Are What We Eat: Healthy Eating Trends from Around the World* (2015) <https://www.nielsen.com/content/dam/nielsenglobal/eu/nielseninsights/pdfs/Nielsen%20Global%20Health%20and%20Wellness%20Report%20-%20January%202015.pdf>.

3. P. Brickman, D. Coates and R. Janoff-Bulman, 'Lottery winners and accident victims: is happiness relative?', *Journal of Personal and Social Psychology*, 36/8 (1978), 917–27.

1

1. Engage Mutual Assurance, *Cost of Dieting* (23rd July 2012) < https://www.onefamily.com/our-story/media-centre/2010/cost-of-dieting/>.

2. Ruben Meerman and Andrew J. Brown, 'When somebody loses weight, where does the fat go?', *British Medical Journal*, 349: g7257 (2014).

3. Traci Mann et al., 'Medicare's search for effective obesity treatments: Diets are not the answer', *American Psychologist*, 62/3 (2007), 220–33.

4. R.L. Leibel et al., 'Changes in energy expenditure resulting from altered body weight', *New England Journal of Medicine*, 332 (1995) 621–8.

5. Marie Ng et al., 'Global, regional, and national prevalence of overweight and obesity in children and adults during 1980–2013: a systematic analysis for the Global Burden of Disease Study 2013', *The Lancet*, 384/9945 (2014), 766–81.

6. P. Gulati et al., 'Fat mass and obesity-related (FTO) shuttles between the nucleus and cytoplasm', *Bioscience Reports*, 34/5 (2014).

7. Neha Alang and Colleen R. Kelly, 'Weight Gain After Fecal Microbiota Transplantation', *Open Forum Infectious Diseases*, 2/1 (2015), doi: 10.1093/ofid/ofv004.

8. S. Hameed et al., 'Thyroid Hormone Receptor Beta in the Ventromedial Hypothalamus Is Essential for the Physiological Regulation of Food Intake and Body Weight', *Cell Reports*, 19/11 (2017), 2202–9.

2

1. Jaymi McCann, 'Takeaway UK: Average Brit is now spending £1,320 a year on fastfood buying 12 meals every month', *Daily Mail* (4 April 2013) <http://www.dailymail.co.uk/news/article-2303861/Takeaway-UK-Average-Brit-spending-1-320-year-fastfood-buying-12-meals-month>.

2. World Health Organization, *Global Health Risks* (2009), <http://www.who.int/healthinfo/global_burden_disease/GlobalHealthRisks_report_part2.pdf>.

3. Roy F. Baumeister and John Tierney, *Willpower: Rediscovering the Greatest Human Strength* (New York: Penguin, 2011).

3

1. Srinivasan S. Pillay, *Life Unlocked: 7 Revolutionary Lessons to Overcome Fear* (New York: Rodale Press, 2010).

2. F. Thielecke et al., 'Determination of total energy expenditure, resting metabolic rate and physical activity in lean and overweight people', *Z Ernahrungswiss*, 36/4 (1997), 310–12.

3. Timothy S. Church et al., 'Effects of different doses of physical activity on cardiorespiratory fitness among sedentary, overweight or obese postmenopausal women with elevated blood pressure: a randomized controlled trial', *JAMA*, 297/19 (2007), 2081–91; E.J. Dhurandhar et al., 'Predicting adult weight change in the real world: a systematic review and meta-analysis accounting for compensatory changes in energy intake or expenditure', *International Journal of Obesity*, 39/8 (2015), 1181–7.

5

1. Mark Hyman, *Eat Fat, Get Thin: Why the Fat We Eat Is the Key to Sustained Weight Loss and Vibrant Health* (New York: Little, Brown and Company, 2016).

2. S. Vandevijvere et al., 'Increased food energy supply as a major driver of the obesity epidemic: a global analysis', *Bulletin of the World Health Organization*, 93 (2015), 446–56.

3. Mark Hyman, *The Blood Sugar Solution* (New York: Little, Brown and Company, 2012).

4. Joanna Blythman, *Swallow This: Serving Up the Food Industry's Darkest Secrets* (London: 4th Estate, 2015).

5. *Jamie's Sugar Rush* (Channel 4) <http://www.channel4.com/programmes/jamies-sugar-rush>.

6. Robb Dunn, 'Science Reveals Why Calorie Counts Are All Wrong', *Scientific American* (1 September 2013) <https://www.scientificamerican.com/article/science-

reveals-why-calorie-counts-are-all-wrong/>; Blythman, *Swallow This*.

7. Brian Wansink et al., 'Slim by Design: Kitchen Counter Correlates of Obesity', *Health, Education & Behavior*, 43/5 (2016), 552–8.

7

1. C. Davis, 'Results of the self-selection of diets by young children', *Canadian Medical Association Journal*, 41 (1939), 257–61.

2. Hallberg, L. et al., 'Iron absorption from Southeast Asian diets. II. Role of various factors that might explain low absorption', *American Journal of Clinical Nutrition*, 30/4 (1977), 539–48.

3. Marc David, *The Slow Down Diet: Eating for Pleasure, Energy, and Weight Loss* (Vermont: Healing Arts Press, 2015).

4. G. P. Smith, 'The Satiety Effect of Cholecystokinin: Recent Program and Current Problems', *Annals of the New York Academy of Sciences*, 448/1 (1985), 417–23.

5. Elizabeth Somer, *Food & Mood: The Complete Guide to Eating Well and Feeling Your Best* (New York: Holt Paperbacks, 1999), 20–3.

6. Ibid., 23–5.

7. Brian Wansink, *Mindless Eating: Why We Eat More Than We Think* (London: Hay House, 2011).

8

1. Shawn Achor, *The Happiness Advantage: The Seven Principles of Positive Psychology that Fuel Success and Performance at Work* (London: Virgin Books, 2011).

2. Martin E. Seligman et al., 'Positive Psychology Progress: Empirical Validation of Interventions', *American Psychologist*, 60/6 (2005), 410–421; Martin E.P. Seligman, *Authentic Happiness: Using the New Positive Psychology to Realize your Potential for Lasting Fulfillment* (Boston: Nicholas Brealey Publishing, 2003).

3. M. Goyal et al., 'Meditation Programs for Psychological Stress and Well-being: A Systematic Review and Meta-analysis', *JAMA Internal Medicine*, 174/3 (2014), 357–68.

4. F. Zeidan et al., 'Mindfulness meditation improves cognition: Evidence of brief mental training', *Consciousness and Cognition*, 19/2 (2010), 597–605.

5. Richard J. Davidson et al., 'Alterations in Brain and Immune Function Produced by Mindfulness Meditation', *Psychosomatic Medicine*, 65/4 (2003), 564–70; W.W. Thaddeus et al., 'Effect of Compassion Meditation on Neuroendocrine, Innate Immune and Behavioural Responses to Psychosocial Stress,' *Psychoneuroendocrinology*, 34/1 (2009), 87–98.

6. D.M. Levy et al., 'Initial results from a study of the effects of meditation on multitasking performance', *CHI '11 Conference on Human Factors in Computing Systems – Proceedings* (2011), 2011–16.

7. Luders, Eileen et al., 'The Underlying Anatomical Correlates of Long-Term Meditation: Larger Hippocampal and Frontal

Volumes of Gray Matter', *NeuroImage*, 45/3 (2009), 672–8.

8. E.R. Albertson et al., 'Self-Compassion and Body Dissatisfaction in Women: A Randomized Controlled Trial of a Brief Meditation Intervention', *Mindfulness*, 6/3 (2015), 444–54.

9. Robert E. Thayer, *Calm Energy: How People Regulate Mood with Food and Exercise* (Oxford: Oxford University Press, 2003).

10. L. DiPietro et al., 'Three 15-min Bouts of Moderate Postmeal Walking Significantly Improves 24-h Glycemic Control in Older People at Risk for Impaired Glucose Tolerance', *Diabetes Care*, 36/10 (2013), 3262–8.

11. C. Esteban et al., 'Influence of changes in physical activity on frequency of hospitalization in chronic obstructive pulmonary disease', *Respirology*, 19/3 (2014), 330–8.

12. Kirk I. Erickson et al., 'Exercise Training Increases Size of Hippocampus and Improves Memory', *Proceedings of the National Academy of Sciences of the United States of America*, 108/7 (2011), 3017–22.

13. P. Gordon-Larsen et al., 'Fifteen-year longitudinal trends in walking patterns and their impact on weight change', *American Journal of Clinical Nutrition*, 89/1 (2008), 19–26.

14. M. Boschmann et al., 'Water-induced thermogenesis', *Journal of Clinical Endocrinology and Metabolism*, 88/12 (2003), 6015–19.

15. T.J. Doyle et al., 'The association of drinking water source and chlorination by-products

with cancer incidence among postmenopausal women in Iowa: a prospective cohort study', *American Journal of Public Health*, 87/7 (1997), 1168–76.

16. J.E. Gangwisch et al., 'Inadequate sleep as a risk factor for obesity: analyses of the NHANES I', *Sleep*, 28/10 (2005), 1289–96.

17. A. Spaeth et al., 'Effects of Experimental Sleep Restriction on Weight Gain, Caloric Intake, and Meal Timing in Healthy Adults', *Sleep*, 36/7 (2013), 981–90.

18. Sunil Sharma and Mani Kavuru, 'Sleep and Metabolism: An Overview', *International Journal of Endocrinology* (2010), doi:10.1155/2010/270832.

19. A.V. Nedeltcheva, et al. 'Insufficient Sleep Undermines Dietary Efforts to Reduce Adiposity', *Annals of Internal Medicine*, 153/7 (2010), 435–41.

20. P.S. Hogenkamp et al., 'Acute sleep deprivation increases portion size and affects food choice in young men', *Psychoneuroendocrinology*, 38/9 (2013), 1668–74.

9

1. Jeffrey A. Cully and Andra L. Teten, *A Therapist's Guide to Brief Cognitive Behavioral Therapy* (Houston: Department of Veterans Affairs South Central MIRECC, 2008).

2. G.M. Manzoni et al. 'Can Relaxation Training Reduce Emotional Eating in Women with Obesity?' *Journal of the American Dietetic Association*, 109/8 (2009), 1427–32; V. Vicennati et al. 'Stress-Related Development of Obesity and Cortisol in Women', *Obesity,* 17/9 (2009), 1678–83.

3. Nicole M. Avenue et al., 'Sugar and Fat Bingeing Have Notable Differences in Addictive-like Behavior', *Journal of Nutrition*, 139/3 (2009), 623–8.

10

1. Adriana D.T. Fabbri and Guy A. Crosby, 'A review of the impact of preparation and cooking on the nutritional quality of vegetables and legumes', *International Journal of Gastronomy and Food Science*, 3 (2016), 2–11.

11

1. Food and Agriculture Organization of the United Nations, *Global Food Losses and Food Waste: Extent, Causes and Prevention* (2011) <http://www.fao.org/docrep/014/mb060e/mb060e00.pdf>.

RECIPES

1. United States Department of Agriculture, *Pesticide Data Program* <https://www.ams.usda.gov/datasets/pdp>.

2. VISA Europe, *17 million UK workers frustrated by cash payments* (2014) <https://www.visaeurope.com/media/pdf/17590.pdf>.

DIGESTIF

1. The Tim Ferris Show, *How to Design a Life – Debbie Millman* <https://tim.blog/2017/01/12/how-to-design-a-life-debbie-millman/>.

FINDING A THERAPIST

1. F. Leichsenring et al., 'The efficacy of short-term psychodynamic psychotherapy in specific psychiatric disorders: A meta-analysis', *Archives of General Psychiatry,* 61 (2004), 1208–16.

2. J.C. Norcross, (2005), 'The psychotherapist's own psychotherapy: Educating and developing psychologists', *American Psychologist*, 60 (2005), 840–50.

3. Jonathan Shedler, 'The Efficacy of Psychodynamic Psychotherapy', *American Psychologist*, 65/2 (2010), 98–109.

ACKNOWLEDGEMENTS

Thank you to:

Liam, for your love, support, patience and faith in everything I do.

Claudia, for making the transition to motherhood so wonderful and for your patience too while I wrote this book. This is for you.

Lorna-Jane, Charles, Olivia, Kim and Sue. Your friendship, advice and encouragement made writing this a truly enjoyable process.

My family, for always believing in me. You have given me the courage to do whatever I put my mind to, including writing this book.

Vanessa Fox O'Loughlin, my agent, for your belief in turning Artful Eating into a book. Your energy and enthusiasm are infectious and there seems to be no end to your knowledge!

The incredible team at Black & White Publishing, you've been so supportive, thoughtful and a joy to work with.

Sean Cahill and Mark Duggan for your beautiful photographs.

I am lucky to have met a few sages along the way, and without their guidance, advice and a little bit of magic, Artful Eating would never have come into being. Thank you Dez McQuaid, Victoria Mary Clarke and Miranda Palmer.

And finally to my wonderful clients. This book is filled with your experiences; some of you are named, some of you I have disguised with new names. Your bravery and courageousness inspired Artful Eating. Thank you from the bottom of my heart.

For more information on Artful Eating, visit

WWW.ARTFUL-EATING.COM

WHERE YOU CAN DOWNLOAD A FREE COGNITIVE AUDIO BUNDLE,
AND SIGN UP TO MY MAILING LIST

ALSO FOLLOW ME ON SOCIAL MEDIA:

TWITTER.COM/KARINAMELVIN
FACEBOOK.COM/ENJOYARTFULEATING
INSTAGRAM.COM/KARINAMELVIN